NORMAN

NORMAN
Mike Freeman

Illustrations by
Juliet Jeffery

© Mike Freeman, 1986

Published by Unit Nine Studios,
Brierley Hill, Staunton, Gloucester GL19 3QR

First published 1986

ISBN 0 9511592 08

Set by Action Typesetting Limited, Gloucester
Printed and bound in Great Britain
by Billing & Sons Ltd., Worcester

CONTENTS

FOREWORD

The story of Norman is one based on fact. Certain parts of his life have had to be filled in with a small amount of fiction as his early youth is now somewhat obscure, although from his arrival at Pen-y-Bont it is well known. It has always been rumoured that his first work was in a mine and I have therefore stuck to this assumption.

All the rest of the story is based on fact and is made up of incidents that really took place. For several years in the early seventies he was an annual feature on both Midland and Harlech television regional news bulletins, pictured with his improvised sleigh, loaded with Christmas trees.

Whilst it is impossible for a horse to converse, they do have some form of communication with one another, and undoubtedly learn to predict events from experience. They also develop characters, many of which have their parallels, good or bad, amongst us higher mortals.

A sheep dog, unoriginally called Shep, and a horse named Grit — both of whom I owned — used to torment each other with great skill. The dog would prance in front of the horse inviting him to race, but only in circumstances where he knew I would not allow it. If he knew a 'canter' was imminent Shep would set off for a head start and would be thoroughly downcast if I called him back to even the odds.

Through exercising the horses and dogs together, Shep knew the area well. Too well at times, so that occasionally he had to be kept on a chain. By leaning over a fence this chain was within reach of Grit. We used to watch in great amusement as the horse picked up the chain and gently tugged it. When the dog could stand it no more he would lunge at the horse's muzzle but always missed by inches, as Grit withdrew with perfect timing. The game lasted long enough for me to capture it on film.

Although these actions, amusing as they may be, are not extraordinary, they do show a certain amount of forethought. My excuse for giving animals the power of human speech is that were I suddenly to become blessed with understanding their animal language, I still could not write this book in their dialect, for nobody would be able to read it. A series of grunts, whinnies and illustrated movements might convey something to an Egyptologist, but nothing useful to anyone else. So, I have chosen the medium we all know and make no apology for it.

There are three forestry terms that recur in the book which require some explanation: a *tush* is the name given to timber that is dragged out of a wood once it has been felled; *thinning* is where some of the trees of a plantation are removed to make way for the others as they grow bigger; *coppice* is where a single tree has been planted, then cut at an early age so that many shoots will grow from the one stump.

Mike Freeman
September 1986

viii

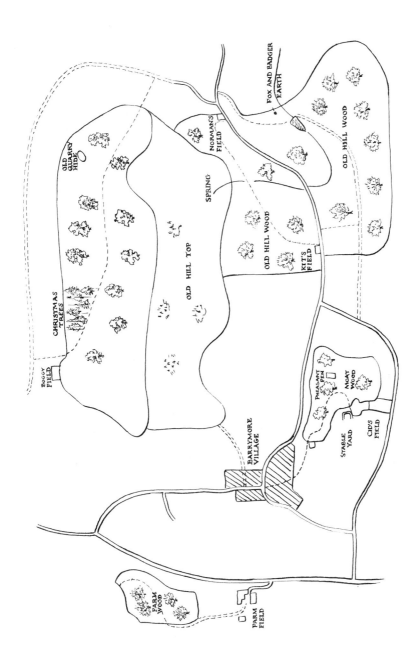

1
LIFE STARTS IN WALES

I hadn't seen a human for three months and then it had only been a fleeting glance.

'Nor-r-maan,' he had shouted, and was quite satisfied when I lifted my head in response.

It had been mild then. The nights cool and refreshing, short in duration, giving way to hot sun in the morning, during which it was comfortable to lie and sleep. By now the nights had extended and were really cold and damp with the dew. Although I had the whole field to myself, there was a shortage of grass. The sweeter grasses had been kept short all through the summer, not only by me but the rabbits as well. Now all that remained were the tall and bitter tufts. It was around these that I was trying to find something more succulent; using my muzzle to push the tall grass out of the way and then nibbling off the younger and shorter growth

1

underneath. It was undoubtedly better to be working, for then I was fed oats. There is no better a feeling than that given by a corn feed at the end of a day's work. Warmth from within reaching out to satisfy tired limbs.

Just now my feet were the biggest source of annoyance. Although it was three months since anybody had seen me, it was a great deal longer than that since I had seen the blacksmith. My feet were now very long, with a tendency to point upwards at their foremost extremity. Three out of the four shoes had fallen off. The length of foot now made moving very difficult, and I had to go around with an exaggerated step, lifting my feet high in the air, to miss the tufts and undulations in the ground. When I caught a foot on something, which was a regular occurrence, then in stumbling I always caught my off fore on the remains of the shoe on my other front hoof. This had stubbornly remained on and, as the hoof grew, so the shoe had twisted round until it now stuck out like a scythe. My muzzle frequently made sharp and painful contact with the earth as I tried to regain my balance, following these stumbles.

The field I was in was totally surrounded by woodland. Sheltered, but very boring. Little sign of life at all; my few fellow creatures had long since run out of anything to say and they were only rabbits and squirrels, for whom the wood provided a hard living. All the interesting forest dwellers were congregated around its edges, from where they could leave under the cover of darkness, and go to different parts to hunt, forage or graze. They always had something new to talk about, some little tale to tell about the night before.

Up here in the back of beyond there was nothing new to tell. The rabbits were dull and the squirrels had little in common with any-one. When I first came to work in woodland, a grey squirrel was a rarity, but now they were everywhere, intent on multiplying and destroying the very trees on which they lived. It was as if the healthy, well-ordered wood was not to their liking, and by damaging the trees so that they bled or broke in half, they would restore it to the worthless wasteland it doubtless had been many years ago. Nobody had much time for the squirrel, a bad-mannered intruder in our countryside.

So long had it been since I last heard a vehicle, other than tractors labouring up some far off hill, that my heart jumped at the high-pitched revving sound in the wood below me. Riveted to the spot, I listened as it got ever closer. The rabbit across the field ceased to eat, flattened its ears and made for the cover of the brambles at the edge of the wood. The noise grew louder and louder, and I could now hear a banging and rattling accompanying it. The slight slope in the field enabled me to move, so that I was just out of sight of the gate.

All had gone quiet when a head and shoulders appeared over the brow. The man walked purposefully towards me, whilst I stood and watched. As he got close his hand reached out but, feeling vulnerable against the edge of the field, I moved more into the open, giving me escape routes in all directions. His hand was still outstretched towards me and the smell of mint reminded me of good times past. I allowed the hand to come closer, until I could take the offered sweet. As I did so another hand came like a shadow, towards my neck. Instantly I dropped my head and, in the same movement, swung away from the danger, up the hill to safety. So unfit was I that this simple manoeuvre left me puffing at the exertion. As if nothing had happened my assailant came on up the hill after me, still at the same unhurried pace. As he drew close the hand was outstretched once more, and I remembered that I had been on the point of taking the sweet. It must have fallen from my mouth when I swung away from him for there was a slight taste left on my muzzle. It was enough for me to want to make sure I took it properly next time. The white shape was still there, so I let his hand come close and then stretched my neck to meet it. This time he stood still and let me take the mint from him. Once it was securely in my mouth I took a step back, but there was no need to do so, for there was no follow-up movement; he just stood and watched as I ate.

When another sweet was offered I allowed him to come closer and, not feeling in any danger from him, let him put his hand over my neck. Whilst eating the second sweet a leather head collar was put on, and a gentle pressure bade me walk towards the gate at the top of the field. Here I found the gate open, but instead of the path beyond, there was now a large dark box almost filling the entire entrance. It was towards this that I was led; right to it, until the man who was leading me started to walk up the ramp that led inside. The rope between us came tight as I remained at the bottom. For the first time the man at my head spoke to me. The voice was gentle and, as he spoke, so a slight pressure was applied to the head collar.

It was now, when I could clearly see him in front of me and had heard his voice, that a certain familiarity came to mind. When another mint was offered, I recalled fields at the bottom of the wood. Summer evenings after work. This man and his family playing around me. His little daughter giggling on my back as she clung to the base of my mane. Her fingers in a vice-like grip, totally out of proportion to one so small. This was Glyn. Glyn, who many years ago worked alongside me in the wood, here at Pen-y-Bont.

The pull on the rope had increased in strength. The leather was now cutting into my neck and under my muzzle. I pulled back and Glyn was forced to follow, the pressure easing. Almost at once Glyn moved back towards the ramp, urging me to come with him. At the same time another man came from the front of the box and applied a light pressure on me from behind. It was clear to me now that it was intended that I should go into the box. So small was it that I doubted I would even fit in it. If I did get in, I knew that there would be no chance that I could ever turn around to get out again. Besides which, it was so dark in there that once in, I doubted I would be able to see at all. The pressure increased again, both from in front and behind. My haunches were almost being lifted off the ground but it was not difficult to remain where I was. The pull and the push both ceased. The man who had been behind me came round to the front and lifted my near fore, pulling it forward and thus putting it down ahead of me so that it came to rest on the ramp. The pressure then increased, holding me in place with the one foot part way up to the box. He then moved to the other side and repeated the process with the offside hoof, but I landed heavily on that foot, sending a rattle through the box. The noise echoed and the ramp itself gave slightly under

4

my weight. Again, despite the pressure on my neck, I came back to the safety of the ground.

Glyn remained on the ramp whilst his companion came to join him. He was a lot taller than Glyn, dressed all in blue and seemingly unworried at my refusal to move further forward; whereas I could detect a certain frustration entering into the hand movements, reflected down the rope that joined Glyn and I.

Mark, as I later came to know him, spent a few minutes trying to relax me. More mints were offered and a lot of patting took place, but all the while I was not allowed to back from the bottom of the ramp. Momentarily Mark left us. When he returned from in front of the box, he was carrying a long length of rope. This was attached to the left-hand side of the box then laid along the ground on that side of me. Slowly Mark picked it up, so that it formed a barrier. He then walked behind me, which allowed the rope to come right under my haunches. Together they pulled, Glyn at my head and Mark at my side. The rope cut into me from behind. It pulled my backside right under me so that I felt that at any moment I would lose balance and topple backwards. All the while there was a hand on my flank, steady and comforting, and a voice urging me to go forward, but not with anger or urgency.

So, it seemed there was little option but to move towards the box. The rope prevented any escape to the left as it did to the rear, whilst Mark was to my right. I took a step forward. The ramp moved under my weight and gave no indication of holding all of me. This one step had given new strength to both Glyn and Mark and, between them, they increased the pressure so suddenly that I had to move on again. This time the ramp felt more solid as both my fore feet came to rest on it. My head was by now almost in the box itself. It was not as dark as I had thought when viewing it from afar, and I could now see into it quite clearly. It was simply a large box. Three quarters of the way inside it there was a bar across and beyond that, a net full of sweet-smelling hay. On the floor was a black mesh, under which were planks of wood. A little light was coming from a small window at the front but the box still seemed too small for me to turn around in, and I could see no way out. The only feature that gave rise to a feeling of security was

5

the smell; there was a strong odour of other horses, so clearly I would not be the first to enter it. With my heart pounding in apprehension, I moved in. Before I even realised I had gone far enough, the rope came away from my side and rear, there was a creaking from underneath me, and what little light there was, seemed to get shut out as the ramp was shut abruptly behind me. It closed with such ferocity and before I was fully in, that I was pushed forward by the leverage and thrown against the breast bar. It groaned in protest but held.

Glyn was still inside the box with me, holding the head-collar rope. Mark now came in through a small door at the front, which cast a sharp light across the box as it was opened. I was made to feel very important and clever at completing such a difficult manoeuvre. This feeling soon evaporated for they both got out shortly afterwards and I was left confined in the darkness that I had originally feared. I tried to turn and see behind me, but my head was tied to the side of the box which allowed only a limited amount of movement. Out of the corner of my eye I could see that the ramp had not completely closed the back, and what little light there was, came between the top of it and the roof. So high was it in proportion to me, that only the tops of the trees were visible. Each twist of my neck or shuffle of a foot made the whole box move violently, and it soon became clear that the less I moved the safer it felt. The small window in front of me was thick with grime but at the right angle it was possible to see a little through it. Enough to see Glyn and Mark get into the car immediately ahead of the box.

The starting of the car sent vibrations under my feet and around the walls. Almost at once the irritating smell of exhaust fumes reached up to my nostrils from the holes in the floor. Then the whole box lurched forward as we all set off down the track. I was grateful then that the box held me in place so tightly, although the noise and irregular movement were terrifying. I could see little and recognised less. Shadows and the tops of trees moved by. The road was rough and we went downhill for a long time. Once on the level, the road became smoother and the movement more regular. I remembered that once before I had travelled in this fashion, although then it had been in something much larger and I had not been alone. For the briefest of moments the memory of that last trip with the rest of the pit ponies sent a shot of adrenalin through my veins. Perhaps there was a subconscious thought that now I was on the move, we might just find ourselves together again after all these years. At the time I thought we were to be inseparable for the rest of our lives. We had shared adjacent stalls underground for three years; taken our two weeks leave above ground in the same field. Finally, we had gone from the pit in the same transport. I was convinced that there had been some terrible mistake when Clyde had been taken out of the lorry and it drove away with me still in it. I wondered what became of him and, as I did so, my thoughts strayed further into the past, to my playmate on the farm where we had both been born . . .

Stallion on the hill had been the most popular game when we were foals. A suitable hillock or tump was chosen as the spot from where the 'stallion' would stand and survey his herd. Other pretenders to the title of King of the Herd would then have to come to the hill and challenge the incumbent. To do this we would come up at a brisk gallop, turn at the bottom of the slope and kick our heels towards the top, to entice him to come down and fight. The fight would mean a good chase around the field, kicking out at each other whilst we ran. Sometimes we would stop and face each other and pretend to fight with our front hooves and teeth, after which it was a straight race back to the highspot, the first to the top taking on the role of 'stallion' until he in turn was challenged and dethroned.

On and off this game could last half a day at a time, unless we were scolded by some of the grumpier members of the herd. If our frolicking came too close to certain members of our group, without any warning they would stretch out their necks, teeth bared, ears flat, and bite us hard. One horse did this with such regularity that he inevitably became an added attraction to the game and, in his case, far from stopping us, made it all the more worthwhile. Just how close could we go to this monster without being in danger of getting a severe nip on the rump? The answer was, of course, that it was closer and closer until the sting of his bite was felt! To start with, we would just let our circuit pass through his part of the field. Even then, although he would continue to graze and show no apparent sign of annoyance, a slight flattening of the ears was enough for us to know that we were getting through to him. What torment we must have inflicted upon that poor animal, although I suspect he was more than aptly rewarded when our bravery exceeded what had been our better judgement, and he caught us with his jaws.

My only occasional thought about the future was as to which one of us would eventually become the leader of the herd. Sometimes, when we were having one of our games, a kick or a bite would come just that little bit closer and a sudden surge within me would cause a violent desire to retaliate in earnest; no longer the playful act, but a genuine urge to do battle, to fight to establish the right to lead, to be respected by all the others.

In time the game based on the hill top was replaced by the dung pile. Instead of leaving droppings anywhere on the high ground where we grazed, all the colts and the stallion came to share the same area. Without us knowing why, it became a ritual to scent all the droppings deposited there, then to stand guard over the site, snorting defiance and pawing the ground. It was still a game to us youngsters but I did notice that we had come under the watchful eye of the stallion who, although he never felt it necessary to exert any domination, would occasionaly wander over to the site when one of us had been showing off for just a bit too long, and without any outward sign of aggression would make us feel rather silly with our false posturing.

Looking back now, I find it strange that I never noticed that there was only the one stallion and that he never had the need to fight for his position at the head of the herd, that he was totally unopposed. Nor was I consciously aware that at any particular stage I lost the desire to take his place, or that our playful pastime ceased.

Weaned from my mother, the need for grazing predominated my life, the same as the rest of the herd. Although we had a large area to roam, the value of the grass was poor and it was important to stock up well before the onset of winter, for it would be a good coat and plenty of fat that would sustain us until the following spring.

We all had our favourite shelters, although it took me a while to understand why mother would move to her particular choice at the onset of poor weather. As the wind increased in strength and the rain came horizontally with it, she would amble over the brow of a hill, heading for the remains of an old stone wall. Most of the wall had long since fallen to the ground but at this one point a group of three small thorn trees had managed to root down through it. Their struggle for survival in the non-nutritious soil had kept them short and wiry, and the roots could be seen at intervals winding to the ground through the cracks in the moss-covered stone that they themselves had helped keep together. All three trees were bent over as if leaning with the wind, even when there was none. The ground beneath them was totally bare, well trodden by the shuffling of hooves through long hours of refuge.

Snow was a rarity, and I associate it most with the coming of spring; the first rays of truly warming sunshine contrasting vividly with the strips of snow still lying out of sight in the hollows, or on the north-facing slopes of hill tops, where only the midsummer sun ever shone. It was when the sun warmed the ground that the buzzards would soar above us, their shrill mono-syllabic cries making them sound so close at hand when in fact they could almost be out of sight. I often watched them for long periods, marvelling at their ability to climb to great heights without a flap of their wings, whereas all other birds appeared to require such an abundance of energy to move through the air.

It was on such a day as this that mother produced my replacement — another foal so damp and pathetic that I did not believe it could possibly live until the next winter, let alone survive it. My sister was to be followed by yet another one before I was taken from them.

2
TWO WEEKS DAYLIGHT A YEAR

Periodically, the herd was mustered together and moved to the farm buildings down in the valley, and that is when I came to be separated from the rest.

I clearly remember being pushed and jostled into a narrow race, bounded on either side by metal poles and only just wide enough for one of us to fit in at a time. At the end was a dark green box, also made of metal, with many panels and perforated with a variety of holes. The horse in front of me surged through and out into the yard at the far end. I struggled to follow, but found my way was barred. When the gate opened again I almost fell to my freedom and rushed to join the others. It was not to be.

They were all there, almost within reach—the whole herd assembled together, but now separated from me by a single row of high fencing. In desperation I went from one end to the other, convinced that somewhere there must be a gap that I had inadvertently got the wrong side of. I remember also the annoyance I felt at the lack of concern shown by the rest, for they merely stood in a bunch, looking back at the men letting through the last few horses.

10

A grating of hooves on the uneven concrete surface announced the arrival of another horse on my side of the fence. Together we raced up and down this barrier tripping over one another at each end. A third was to join us just before the rest were returned to the higher grazing grounds. I was thankful that, at least, I had some company for what seemed to be a long wait.

When the men returned we were ushered into a small shed, whereupon the three men present leant over the door and gazed at us. There was a lot of discussion before one of them came into the shed with us. He was an old man of huge proportions, his fawn-coloured coat making him almost square in outline, a well-chewed cigar and peak cap providing the only sharp features to a rounded face. He moved amongst us with a rocking motion, grunting and prodding with a stout stick. After a moment's silent contemplation, he turned to the other two men, nodded, and made his way to the door. All three then left, leaving us cowering and terrified at the back of the shed. It was already getting dark when a lump of mouldy hay was thrown over the door and we were left alone for the night.

The following morning we were overjoyed to hear the approach of hooves. A large bay shire horse appeared in the yard outside and we were almost instantly let out to join it. As it was led out into the road, we followed. Down the road and all the way to a farm that I had never seen before, all three of us dutifully pursued it. This place was totally different from the one I had just come from. There were no large buildings nor areas of concrete. Small stables dominated the yard, most of them occupied by horses who stared out at the new arrivals.

I was cajoled into a brick-and-timber stable, large enough for only one horse. There were other horses on either side of me, each of us separated by a low partition of timber panelling. All the wood along the tops of these divisions had been scalloped by years of chewing, as had the top of the door and the frame in which it precariously hung. The floor had a covering of straw, and hay was waiting for me in the far corner. I had no idea that horses lived in such comfort.

Humans were around us all the time from dawn until dusk, and the rotund gentleman who had come to the farm was often to be seen leaning on his stick in the middle of the yard, constantly issuing orders to those around him. Whenever I was led out he would be much in evidence, and was quite clearly supervising on the first occasion a full harness was fitted on me. With a bit more of the tack being added each day, it seemed only a short time before a young boy was trying to back me in between the shafts of a small cart.

The initial terror of the rattling pursuit behind me, no matter what I did or where I went, is still a vivid memory. The fitting of the harness, the yoke and even the shafts had all been accomplished without any problems, but this latest development had been a major upset that took more than the one day to overcome. I have to confess that once that initial fright had been dispensed with, what followed was pure enjoyment. Every morning I would be backed into the shafts and taken for a drive around the lanes. Each time a new instruction was introduced until I would turn left or right, stop or reverse, speed up or slow down, all at a verbal command, until finally there seemed to be nothing more to be learned.

Indeed there had been nothing more to be learned, for shortly afterwards I and two others from the same yard were collected by lorry and taken to our new place of work, and what a dramatic change it turned out to be.

When the rear ramp was let down all we could see was blackness. The ground was black, as were the buildings, the hills also, and all around were more heaps of black. Even the men wore black clothing. No sooner had we been taken from the transport than we were led to the cage. The doors slid to with a crash, and the long descent commenced. The stark white light from the overcast sky rapidly changed to a mellow amber as the artificial lighting took over and the other was sliced off at the top of the shaft. When the gates opened again at the bottom, it was to let us out into a different world. A world where there was nothing that could not be easily touched. There was no distance to look into, nothing beyond the immediate vicinity. If anything happened of interest it either passed you by, or involved you.

From the shaft I was led along narrow, low passages with un-even floors. The air was damp and warm, the surroundings blacker than ever. The last corner, though, revealed a great shock, for suddenly far underground, in a black world that forced upon one a feeling of loneliness and isolation, all was now white. Whitewashed walls, whitewashed stalls, scrubbed floors and a smell of hay. As I was led along past the other horses, I could see that each stall had a manger and a name written on the curved wall above. I was taken straight to the stall that was to be my permanent home for the next three years. Clyde was my neighbour, on the left-hand side.

When I first saw him he struck me as being very strange, but the following morning I was to find that I, too, would lose all my tail and mane, as well as being clipped out all over. This was due to the presence of dust in the air which, had not all our coat been removed, would have caused considerable irritation and sores, despite the fact that I was to be regularly groomed both before and after work, as were all the other horses working in this mine.

The second shock was the tack that I would have to wear while working below ground. Because the passages were so narrow and low, I had to have a large piece of leather attached to the bridle and covering the top of my head. In addition, I had to wear blinkers—not that there was anything frightening to either side—but to protect me from damaging an eye against walls on either side of me.

There were horses of all sizes in those underground stables; just as the passages themselves varied in size, so the horses were matched to the area in which they were to work. None of us had a lot of extra space around us, and all wore the same protective leather which bore the scars to vouch for its necessity.

'I am surprised they have brought in you youngsters,' said Clyde on my second day in the mine.

'The rumours around here are that we will all be out of work before long.'

'There seems more than enough of that for all of you and several more,' I replied, thinking of all the activity and bustle I had already seen in my one day below ground.

'There's not one of us worked a new shaft since the last holiday,' Clyde told me, 'Although there are new shafts, I've seen them, but you couldn't fit a horse in any of them. Full to the brim with machinery they are and the coal running down the middle of them like it was a mountain stream.' A firm nod of the head ended the sentence on a factual note.

'I came with a lorry load of others,' I told him, trying to sound hopeful about the prospects.

'This place used to be full to the end of the stalls. Look at it now—only just over half of them occupied.' He glanced beyond me in the direction of the vacant stalls and I, too, followed his gaze. Indeed there was room for plenty more of us.

'If all of those were full where have the horses gone?' I asked him.

'Rumours. The whole place is full of rumours,' he muttered.

'Rumours about what, Clyde?'

'About where the horses have gone,' he said. 'I tell you, the slightest injury or sign of lameness, and you are out. No second chance. There was a time when you could be laid up down here. The vet would come and attend to you and a spare horse would do your work for a while. Not now though. First bit of trouble and off you go.'

'Off you go to where?' I asked again.

'That's where the rumours come from. Nobody really knows, but you don't come back here and you don't end up on the holiday fields as some of the more serious injuries used to. It has come back via the bush telegraph that we all get loaded up into lorries and taken down to the sea.' I waited, expecting him to say more.

'Taken to the sea, and then what?' I felt he must have heard a bit more than that.

'Just seem to disappear,' he said despondently. 'There have been all sorts of stories around, but not one of them makes it sound as if there is anything worthwhile.' He sighed in resignation, then continued, 'I had thought that if the work ran out we might be allowed to stay in the holiday fields, but they are getting fewer at the same time as we do, so it doesn't seem very likely.'

14

'I can tell you, Clyde, that there were many of us who came to this mine yesterday. What is more, I have come straight from the outside world to this. Just a short while on a farm and then here. No work before of any sort.' He looked happier at this. 'Anyway, why would it matter if you left?' I went on. 'It must be better working up on the surface, in the fresh air.' I had yet to get used to the close atmosphere that existed below ground.

'Why work at all?' The voice came from the stall to my right. I turned to look at him but found myself stuck for a suitable reply. 'I agree with being up in the air but can't see any sense in working up there as well.' He confirmed his original opinion. 'Don't actually do a lot down here if I can possibly avoid it,' he added.

A chorus of laughter echoed down the horse lines at his last remark and it would not be long before I got to see why. His aim in life was to avoid work himself, whilst at the same time creating it for others. Every morning his handler had difficulty in getting him to back out of his stall. When he had got him out he again had trouble making him move off. He would stand there as if rooted to the spot, only his head and neck flexing enough to take the strain of each fresh attempt to get him underway. If the handler went round behind him to whack him into motion, he would turn to face him afresh. If he tried to hold his head and at the same time get the stick to his backside, the pair would end up following each other around in a sort of ritual dance. Occasionally just as the handler thought he had won and the horse took a few steps, it would amount to just that and the whole game would commence again, but four or five stalls further up the lines.

We would get a thorough grooming both before and after work, and sooner or later a brush would be placed on the partition between us. Within seconds a 'clonk' would signify that it had fallen to the floor, having been gently helped on its way by our friend. The handler would invariably hit him and remember not to place it back on the partition but, since it was the most convenient place for keeping it when hands were required for something else, it would not be long before another 'clonk' would record the brush falling to the floor once more.

When his handler went in to groom him you could guarantee that if he didn't get squashed against the partition on the way in, he would soon be letting out a yell as his foot was trodden firmly into the ground. The amazing thing was that all these happenings appeared to be genuine mishaps. The horse never moved with great deliberation and certainly not with any sign of speed. His punishment was therefore never severe.

He was not past refusing to move once he was harnessed to the coal trolleys. Sometimes, when the loaders set about him for it, he would simply back away from them until he came back on the trolley itself. If they didn't stop then, he would continue back, pushing the trolley behind him. Once, he decided to back up for no reason at all, other than mischievousness, whilst the trolley was still being loaded. No-one apparently noticed what was happening−not, that is, until a shovelful missed the trolley altogether and fell fair and square on the horse himself. Thinking that this was some new form of reprisal he shot forward with great haste, taking his tow with him once the chains came tight. It could not have been more than half full, for they apparently left the site at a great pace. Where that shaft joined another, there was a junction of the rails, and here the trolley foundered. The horse made it around the corner but the load did not, the junction and the bend contriving to tip it all over.

First on the scene was a supervisor who, having heard the crash, got there before the pursuing loaders. Seeing the terrified horse with marks on its back and neck from the lumps of coal, he immediately assumed that these had been made by them being thrown at it. Accordingly he made the loaders pick up all the coal by hand and then push the trolley back to its original position before harnessing the horse to it again, all the while consoling the animal for what had been done to it!

There were ten of us who shared the same groom and I like to think that he was as fond of us as we were of him. Anybody could come walking down the passage towards us and it is doubtful that even a single ear would be pricked amongst the lot of us. There was, though, an unofficial competition to see who could first identify the approach of Tommy. He was a cheerful man and the uneven bounce of his walk reflected in the echo of his footsteps. Should there be any doubt from the sound of his tread, it would soon be dispelled when we heard him tapping his palms on his thighs as he strode along. He never failed to get a reception of ten assorted whinnies whenever he came in sight. Although we got to know our handlers just as well, there was never the same sort of bond between us as there was with Tommy. Also, the handlers were occasionally changed, but Tommy was the one who looked after me from the time I arrived to the day I left.

Clyde, of course, knew him well when I first came, and initially I had no idea why he would whinny for no obvious reason or stand gazing fixedly down the line. I never had to ask why, for the reason soon became apparent, although I could never have guessed that any human could come to mean so much to a horse.

The only time we weren't able to see Tommy regularly was when we were on our annual holiday. This was the highlight of every year; the time from which all other time was taken. Any other event of significance was either just before, a long time after or any other time phase, but always relevant to our holiday above ground. When I had first been told about this great happening I was unimpressed. Two weeks in a field, so what? I had just spent three years in a field. Later I was to change my opinion completely.

The build-up to that holiday fortnight was frenzied. We all knew what was imminent. The miners themselves were our best indicators. Voices became louder, laughter echoed through the underground chambers, and their gesticulations became ever more flamboyant. The rate of work dropped off as the loaders spent more and more time in excited conversation. Many a time, through sheer force of habit, I would move off with the trolley long before it had been filled to capacity. No cursing, no shouts or hail of coal, just hoots of laughter at my supposed impatience.

How brilliant the light was when we finally got to the top of the shaft, the winding gear standing out in sharp relief against the white-speckled blue sky. Before we had even left the site, the scent of summer had invaded our nostrils, our senses alert to any smell other than coal dust and stable odour.

17

We pranced and played about like so many stallions awaiting the start of a race. Chubby shapes with no tails or manes, short in the leg and large in the rump, but we all felt as a sixteen-hand thoroughbred must. As the buckle on the head collar was released, I pulled my head away and raced the length of the field and back. Like a wild herd we ran; bucking, kicking and snorting our defiance at anything or anyone who cared to notice. The faster I ran the greater the exhilaration and the greater the exhilaration, the more my desire to run increased. Not until every muscle in the body was totally drained did any of us relax to sample the delight of fresh grass.

Although it was normal practice to let us out onto the aftermath of a hay or silage crop, the freshness still contrasted vividly with the dry and dusty food that we had been used to. Each bite released its own sharp flavour, the juices from the clover forcing the taste buds back into action as the tang percolated through the mouth and under sensitive tongues.

Following the initial stampede, most of the horses formed into social groups, usually based upon the neighbours each had in the stalls. I was no exception, Clyde and I always being together and joining up with another pairing from the far end of the horse lines, one of whom Clyde regularly worked with, as they were of exactly the same size. Many groups were larger than four, but often had battles amongst themselves over the right to choose the best spot to graze. We found no animosity amongst ourselves, grazing and lazing in utter bliss.

3
INTRODUCTION TO GLOUCESTERSHIRE

So deep in my past had my thoughts been buried, that I had failed to notice that all movement had stopped. There was sudden, complete silence, then Glyn and Mark's conversation grew louder as they came closer to the trailer. The small door opened and Glyn got into the trailer. He made a big fuss of me, almost as if he were surprised to find that I was still there after all that time. There were some rattles and the groaning of reluctant hinges from behind, and daylight flooded back in. Glyn untied the rope and rested a hand on my shoulder and at the same time I felt a slight tug on my tail. I tried to turn around and see behind me, but I was too restricted and the brightness of the light outside made it extremely difficult. Cautiously I put a hind leg back, and finding the ramp I continued to reverse out, until my hind legs slid uncertainly off the end onto the brick-surfaced yard. There I remained, surveying my new surroundings.

I could not see very far in any direction for I was in the middle of a three-sided yard. On my right was a large garage made of red brick with carved stone work surrounding the doorway. To the side of the door and carved from matching stone, was a water trough. On my left was a plain brick wall, out of the top of which grew a small tree whose roots were woven in and out of the pointing. By leaning to one side and around the trailer, I could see that ahead of me were two stables. Large and airy, they were divided from one another by a stout timber partition, on top of which was mounted a cast-iron balustrade. Three enormous cast pillars were to the right, left and centre, and I could see through the one open door to a fresh-laid bed of golden straw. At that moment the pressure on the head collar increased, and I was led to that very stable. The bed was just as deep and fresh as it had looked from further off, but the stable appeared even larger and would easily have accommodated four working horses under-ground. I was still investigating my new surroundings when the sound of a metal bucket drew my immediate attention towards the doorway. The bucket matched the baronial proportions of the stables and was put on the floor with a generous covering of oats in the bottom. No-one else came until dusk, when Mark appeared and threw in some fresh hay and replenished the water. A pat on the neck and a mint was then the last I saw of him till morning.

It was well into the next day before he returned, and with the aid of some tools took off the remaining shoe. After which I was led out of the stable and down a lane with a tall hedge on one side and a steep bank on the other. Gradually the bank got lower and I could see that on the other side there was a belt of chestnut trees, planted in an orderly pattern and now grown to a height of between ten and fifteen metres. so that it was quite possible to see through them into the field beyond. A field where the grass looked fresher than any I had seen for a long time, and I instantly hoped I would be put onto it.

No sooner had the thought crossed my mind than we came to a track running between the trees, leading into the field itself. As I was led up it I could see how big the field was. Directly in front of me was a wicket gate, to the right of which ran a post and rail fence dividing the one field from another lower down the slope of the land. Set into the fence was a water trough, the ground around it well trodden and bereft of growth.

I was still trying to take it all in when I realised that Mark was walking away from me, swinging the head collar from his right hand. The slope was greater than I had first thought but I bounced to the brow, nonetheless. To my right the field curved around a cherry tree, forming a large bay against the background of dense woodland. To the left of the flat plateau in front of me, the ground fell away out of sight, where the chestnut trees I had just come through ended. On the corner grew a much older and more majestic chestnut, one whose branches defied gravity and grew out horizontal to the ground, providing shelter from the sun and flies in the height of summer. One indeed that was used for that very purpose, for below it dry and scattered were the remains of many horse droppings. I was not alone!

Moving towards this tree the remaining part of the field started to unfold before me. In fact it went back down the hill to within a few metres of the stables where I had just spent the last night. Also, lined up looking over the fence at the yard were three horses. As if feeling my staring presence behind them, they turned as one and cantered towards me.

We sniffed and snorted and blew up each others' nostrils in turn, before setting off around the field at a gallop. They were all of considerably slimmer build than I and made much lighter work of the hills. Each time we mercifully came to a halt, one or other of them would kick his heels in the air to signal the start of another lap.

One of the three was a thoroughbred, and surprisingly it was he who was the first to break away and go to the shade of the chestnut tree, whilst the rest of us set off on yet another wild chase. The next to drop out was the large bay horse who lost interest in the game, although I suspect he was probably the fastest and fittest of the trio. The last of that group was a dark bay of medium build who did not seem to know what it was to get tired, and kept me going until I ached all over and was compelled to halt. My lungs felt as if they were working up my throat to get closer to the supply of oxygen. Sweat poured down my neck and dripped to the

21

ground between my front legs as I dragged myself over to the tree. The bay and the thoroughbred had taken up stations alongside each other, so that the swishing action of their tails would keep the flies off each other's face. Neither seemed to notice my arrival. Cid, as the dark bay was called, stood his ground in the middle of the field and snorted his defiance at those who would no longer partake in his game. Once completely assured that no one was going to continue, his head sank and he ambled over to join us in the shade.

'Hello' he mumbled, much more out of breath than he would have had us believe.

'What keeps you so fit?' I asked in genuine bewilderment,

'I think it must be the best job us horses can do,' said Cid. 'Not that I care for all the travelling very much but, once we're there, it's just like being in a herd. Sometimes we roam across miles and miles of countryside. On a good day we all go flat out across fields and jump the hedges and ditches to get from one to the other.'

I could see his eyes light up as he spoke. It clearly meant a great deal to him.

'All of us go hunting,' he said, 'Even that miserable has-been.' This was said with a swing of his head towards the thoroughbred, who turned out to be called Hatty.

'You enjoy this hunting as well, then?' I enquired of Hatty.

'Bloody disorganised if you ask me,' came the reply. 'There are no rules, you just go where you like, when you like. All the heaviest horses get through the gates first. If you try and push in you get kicked or trodden on. Most of them are so thick they don't feel any pain—crash through anything, hedges, ditches, even gates. Don't give a damn about anyone. Not like racing. Now that's what we horses were really meant for.'

This little outburst had rather caught us by surprise, and I got the impression that it was probably more than he had had to say for the last month or so. Feeling responsible for evoking it in the first place, I felt duty bound to break the silence.

'You like racing, then?' I enquired.

'Not much. Can't see any sense in it. All that running, just to end up where you set out from.'

22

'Oh' I said, having expected a long lecture on the virtues of the sport of kings.

'Don't worry about him' said Cid, 'he's only here until someone can pluck up the courage to have him . . .'

'Do shut up,' interrupted Mole, the last of the trio, who seemed more intent on his siesta than anything else. Cid produced a big theatrical sigh and moved off to graze and, feeling three was a crowd under the tree, I followed him out into the sunshine. As I drew alongside I asked what he had meant to say before he had been interrupted.

'Nothing much,' he replied. 'I can see from your shape that you are not here to come hunting with us.' This was more of a statement than a question, for he went on, 'What actually do you do?'

I briefly outlined how I was harnessed to a log or tush of several small trees in order to pull them out of the wood or to where they were to be sawn.

'Kit does that here,' he said. 'Great girl she is—must be twice my size. Feet on her you could eat your oats out of it they were upturned.' He looked impressed at the thought of what he had just said. 'Been here longer than I have. Part of the place really. Just wait till you meet her—coloured mare she is, with the wit and temper that you would expect from a gypsy lady. Can't imagine why they'd want you as well, though.' He paused for thought and then added, 'Unless there's something wrong with her. She might even be having a foal, you never know.'

As it turned out I didn't have to wait long before meeting this famous lady, for one afternoon about a week after my arrival at Barrymore, all four of us heard the familiar clip-clop of hooves. As was usual on these occasions, we stood on the skyline to see who was going along the lane, which could be seen at the bottom of the lower field, and there she was, all fitted out with the collar and chains of a tushing horse. As she neared the gate to the lower field her rider made vigorous attempts to stop her but opted for jumping off and catching the bridle just above the bit. He then opened the gate, took off all her tack and let her loose. She must have known we were all watching for she set off up the field in a

23

magnificent trot for one so large. She held her tail high and swung her head from side to side, making the white mane flow out as she did so. I was sure I could feel the vibration of her footsteps right at the top of the hill. She reached the fence before any of us had moved. Three of us went down to meet her—Hatty remaining unmoved by her display. I could tell that I was the centre of her attention as we all approached, and she squealed and stamped her feet as I reached over the fence to blow in her nose. It was quite difficult to know in what direction she was looking for her eyes appeared to have pupils that were off-centre, besides which the eyeball was small in relation to the size of the eye as a whole, so that there was a large area of white all around it. Her muzzle was broad and pink, whilst her hair flowed over her large feet. Otherwise she was as Cid had described her—large and coloured. With a squeal she reared and swung away from us to describe a circle before returning to the fence.

'Are you bleedin' lot going to join me, or does this old lady have to try and get over that there fence?' she enquired.

Mole never said a word and didn't look as if he meant to reply to such a stupid suggestion, whilst Cid muttered something to the effect that he was quite happy where he was. Feeling I could do better than that, I eyed the fence but, before I had made a move, Kit had left us and, having moved away from the fence, was now lining up for it at a canter. As she got closer so the pace of her approach got slower, until at the last stride she appeared to come to a halt. Then, rising like a great white whale from the depths of the ocean, her front legs went up and over the top rail. The rest of her body didn't follow so her rib cage smashed on the rail, which snapped in two as if it were matchwood. Gathering together as much grace as possible in the circumstances, the mare lifted her enormous hind hooves over the lower rails and turned to join us.

'Well, now I am here, what have you got to tell me? What's an 'orse abaht as broad as it's long doing in this posh field anyway?'

I drew a breath to explain, but she went on, 'You be lookin' as if you should be in wood along wi' me.'

'That's just what I do.'

24

'Well, there's only work for one of us 'ere,' she said defensively.

'What's the work like here then? Do you have good handler?'

These questions set us off into a long conversation such as is only possible between two who share the same work or hobby. We grazed and talked most of the night, wandering around the field, two abreast. I don't even recall seeing the other three again. The work, although very similar, seemed more consistent than that at Pen-y-Bont, but her handler didn't seem to have much sympathy for her needs. Equally, she didn't have much feeling for him and clearly felt she knew more about her work than he did and, accordingly, made most of the decisions during the day without him even realising she was doing so.

'I am getting tired of this work, though' she confided. 'It must be twelve or thirteen years since I started on this Estate and I was no chicken when I came here. I bet these folk think this was my first job, but I pulled a ruddy cart around a farm plenty long enough before this.'

'That's funny; I used to pull a little cart in a coal mine before I did this. Not for very long, though, as they were already going electric when I started.'

'I 'ated just being between shafts, didn't you?' she asked. But before I had replied, went on, 'No initiative required at all, merely go where you were told, when you were told. Bloody boring. Hated every minute of it. Glad to get away from the old fool who owned me, too. Never called me anything but "Mare". "Whoa, Mare. Back, Mare. Gee up, Mare. Stand still, Mare. Stand bloody still when I tell you, Mare", and the whip would come stinging across my rump. Oh no! I'd rather this, any day. I reckon you must have been just as glad to get out of the mine, weren't you?' she asked.

'Oh, I was in a way.'

'Why only a way? It's said to be one of the worst jobs going.'

'Maybe,' I replied, not wishing to disagree, 'But at the time there wasn't any other work for us pit ponies and the rumours going around the mine made it seem a privilege to stay on.'

'What sort of rumours?' she asked.

'Well, towards the end, we were going off by the lorry load, a dozen or more at a time. It was said that the lorries went down to the sea and all the horses were put onto a boat along with lots of others from various parts of the country. Those that got to the other side of the water alive, for quite a few died on the way, were then taken to a market. There they were sold alongside cattle, sheep and pigs, just as if they were stupid farm animals, only destined to live a few years and bred for meat.'

'Was that really true?' she asked.

'I never did find out for sure, but one of the other rumours at the time was that we would leave the pit to go to a farm where there was no work at all. There we would all be put in an enormous field and left, until we were near to death, when we would be taken somewhere even worse.' I went on, 'This I know was almost true for, one day at Pen-y-Bont, an old lady came through the woods riding a small stocky pony. Seeing me in my field she came up and gave me a pat, tied her pony to the gate and sat down to have her picnic lunch. During this time I got talking to the pony and it turned out that he was by then twenty-seven years old but he, too, had started work in the pits. When his pit went electric he was taken to just such a farm.'

'How come he was in the middle of the wood with you, then?' she urged me to continue.

'Well, when he got to this farm, it was exactly what we all thought. All the ponies were thrown in together and, although the oldest ones said that they had been well cared for at the beginning, as the numbers increased so they were given less and less attention. There was no work, very little to eat, and a lot of disease which took a strong hold in the overcrowded conditions, He told me that every pony had worms and feet disorders of one sort or another, whilst many had severe skin rashes as well.' I paused to reflect on my luck at avoiding such a fate.

'Did he break out, then?' she kept me going, eager to know more.

'No, it seemed they never even contemplated such a thing. Morale was too low for any of them to even try to improve themselves. He had been lucky, for now and then someone would come amongst them, select a pony and be allowed to take it away.'

'He must have been eternally grateful to that old lady,' she said with feeling.

'He certainly was, and he thought the world of her. He told me they used to share everything when they went on long rides. Sometimes the two of them would pack up and leave for a week or more, just travelling the lanes and tracks through the Welsh mountains.'

'Wouldn't it be lovely if we all did that at the end of our working days . . .' Kit was already dreaming of it. 'Not from bloody 'ere, you won't,' she added, coming back to reality with a crash.

'Nor from anywhere else,' I replied in a matter-of-fact tone and then went on, 'But you can see now why I didn't really want to leave the mine. It was, after all, work; we were all fed, looked after and there was a lot of comradeship amongst us ponies. Plenty to talk about at the end of each day. Yes, the work was hard and dirty but it wasn't a bad life.'

'Do you prefer the work in the wood?' asked Kit.

'Ah, yes, now I feel just the same as you, but I didn't when I was in the mines and had no idea what lay in store for me.'

'I'm glad you're here though,' she said, returning to the original topic. 'At least you can take some of the pressure of work off my back.'

'I really would like to do that, Kit,' I said in all sincerity. I began to feel like a real gentleman.

'Yes, you would at that, wouldn't you?' Her strange eyes had a warmth to them I hadn't noticed before. 'It ain't up to you, though, is it, lad?'

'What if you were to show that you didn't feel well? Surely then they would come and get me to do your work for a bit, wouldn't they?'

'Might. Might not. But I reckon it's what yer 'ere for. Them fools have tried to get me in foal, you know.'

'Oh, when was that?' I asked.

'Recently—don't know my age, see, else they'd never try.'

'Isn't it just possible that you are in foal?' I enquired.

'Not a chance, fella, not a chance. Nice thought, though, eh?' I wasn't sure. Although if it made her happy yes, then it was, and

27

I agreed with her by way of a meaningful nod. She continued, 'A few years back it would have been great.' She drifted into a dream-world. 'I always imagined having a foal at foot, working in the wood with my baby at my side. Watching him play amongst the trees as I worked, letting him suckle between the loads then, later on, teaching him the work so that in time he could take my place in the chains.' Her eyes had gone out of focus as her imagination took over. 'Don't think I am not happy with my life.' She turned to look at me again, 'It's just that . . . well, I suppose I would be proud and satisfied to have produced a foal who had taken over from me.'

'Never mind, Kit, there are many a lot worse off than you and I.' This staid old line was meant to comfort her in some way.

'You and me ain't bad off, Norman. No, not bad off at all.'

Despite the fact that we hadn't known each other long, I felt that in the short time we had built a very strong bond between us and I already dreaded the morning when I suspected she would have to go to work. But it was good to know that, here at Barry-more, there was someone with whom I could share a common interest and that sooner or later, we would be bound to meet over a gate or hedge, if not share a field for a day or two. As the sun rose over the distant Cotswold escarpment, we both fell asleep on our feet.

It seemed only a short time later that Matt, her handler, came to take her to work. That she had moved herself to the top field didn't seem to cause any surprise when he collected her. I followed her as far as the gate and whinnied a soft farewell.

It must have been a month before I saw her again. I had just been caught and put in chains for the first time at Barrymore and was in the process of being moved to another part of the Estate, when I came to a field on the edge of one of the woods and there, sheltering in the corner, was Kit. Her head hung low and I could see all her ribs, whilst her haunches stood out like those of black and white cows. Near where she stood was a shed, and Matt stopped here for a bite to eat. I moved over to Kit and enquired after her health. It appeared that she felt so tired that she could no longer do a proper day's work, which is why I had been put into harness. But, before we could talk more, I was led away.

Kit's field, as I came to know it, was at the bottom of the wood, with the public road on one side and a track going up the wood on the other and it was on this track that I was taken to work. Although I was close to her field all day I was not taken back past her, but along a track through the middle of the wood into another field, which was also new to me. Over the next few years this was to become my permanent base, although I would at times go into other fields which were more convenient to where I was working.

The following day I was collected in the morning and taken back to work in the same area as before, but I didn't know whether I would be able to get down to see Kit or not. When the time came for Matt's morning break, I hoped he might have gone down to the hut by her field again, but he seemed to be in a big hurry with his work and only stopped for a few minutes. We worked fast all day, with only very short breaks, which was very hard for me as it was only my second day at work in nearly a year and I was totally unfit but, clearly, this was of no concern to Matt. He pushed me to the limit of my endurance, to such an extent that all I could think of in the afternoon was the time for Matt to go home. Only when I got back to the field that evening did I again think of Kit; what might be wrong with her, and how very much I wanted to see her again.

I expected to be caught for work again the next morning but nobody came—not until midday, when Glyn appeared with some oats which I took to be some reward for the labours of the day before. He was also my only visitor on the following day, when he gave me another helping of oats. Early the next morning it was Matt who came, but there didn't seem to be the same degree of urgency about him as before, and we went to work at a more leisurely pace. I learned later that, not given to hard work by nature, Matt would always start the week at a slow rate but, as Friday approached, so he realised that insufficient work had been done to make a living wage and that all wasted time from the whole week had to be made up in one go, as his wages at the end of the week were in relation to the amount of timber moved by the pair of us. I always felt this system was rather hard on me, but it was Matt who was to go to an early grave, so perhaps it was just as taxing on him. It did at least mean that, on this day, we had time to spare and I was delighted when, at 10 o'clock, we set off down the track to the shed by Kit's field. As we approached I tried hard to see if she was there, but much to my disappointment there was no sign of her. When Matt had settled by the shed to eat his bread and cheese, I worked my way over to the hedge just to make sure. Up against the wood there was a huddle of people, either bent over or kneeling, by what I could just make out to be Kit, lying on the ground. I knew straight away that there must be something seriously wrong, for horses do not like to have humans near them when they are lying down and will get up as soon as they come within close range. Feeling that I must know more, I started walking around the field to get near her, but Matt was quick to come and catch me. Although I resisted strongly he led me back to the shed where, instead of settling back to his meal, he packed it away and took me up into the wood.

Later that morning and during the afternoon I made several attempts to escape and get back down to Kit, but Matt had no confidence in me and would not let me go, except when I was harnessed to a tush. I contemplated taking the whole lot with me but was frightened of the consequences of going downhill at any great speed with a tree attached to me—rightly so, as I was to learn not long afterwards.

It was late in the day when, above all the noise of the chains and the snapping of branches, there was a muffled report from the bottom of the wood. It was not a noise I had ever heard before, and yet it sent a shiver down my spine. Matt had also heard it and paused momentarily, before resuming work.

For what was left of the afternoon I worked on slowly, oblivious to the pressure from Matt. I was not even working hard enough to keep out the cold and damp which was now creeping into the wood as the strength went out of the sun, flickering as it fell behind the trees. We didn't go straight back to my field at the end of that day, but went back down to Kit's. There was no sign of her but Glyn was at the shed collecting bits of harness, and Matt stopped to talk to him. Feeling his grip loosen on the bridle

I pulled gently away. He didn't stop me, so I went over the the hedge where I had seen Kit earlier. There was no sign of her now, only the flattened patch of grass where she had lain with a small splash of blood at one end of it. Leading across the field from this patch was a broad line going to the gate by the roadside, indicating where they had dragged her to the waiting lorry. Matt took me slowly back to my field, produced a large helping of oats and even offered me some of his bread. He actually gave me a pat before leaving, the only sign of affection he had ever shown, and it was only to happen once more in the years we were to work together.

Kit's death had saddened me greatly and I would have loved to have left my field for a while, if only to have gone back and told the others about what I had seen and heard that day. I remembered what Cid has started to say about Hatty . . . 'Pluck up the courage to have him . . .' Did any of us die a natural death? I wondered. Would I have to keep working for ever so as to avoid such an ending, or would I have a period of genuine retirement? My field was barely fenced at all, so that many times I contemplated an escape but, somehow, I never actually took the final step, although nearly every day when I was out at work I would plan just where and when I would go. But, in the peace of the evening, nothing ever came of it.

As well as working all day I spent much of the night foraging, and it was thus all rather galling when some scruffy sheep started to share my field and compete with me for what little grazing there was. Nothing would happen until after dark, but then quite regularly, a small lorry would pull up outside the gate. Out got the driver who would go round to the back, let down the ramp, and out came twenty ewes. They came straight to the gate, pushing and shoving at each other until the driver let them into my field. At first I thought this to be an official delivery, but just after dawn, long before anyone was around, the lorry returned. Again the ramp was let down and the gate opened, and in came a sheep dog. The sheep knew the drill to perfection and at the sight of the dog gathered into a bunch, made their way out through the gate and got straight into the lorry. Matt and Glyn must have thought

I had a ferocious appetite, for the field was permanently bare. It took on a burnt-yellow look, instead of a healthy green.

'This is all I have, you know,' I would protest to the ewes.

'That's more than we have, mate,' or 'Make the most of it while you can' would be the sort of reply from the more polite amongst them. Once I stood in the middle of the field and shouted at them all–'Look, ladies,' which started a chorus of titters, 'I have to go to work every day and I can't do that if you lot come and eat all my food. It takes a lot of energy to do my work. I need the grass and the rest, so please clear off!'

They barely paused in their bid to remove every available blade of grass before sun-up. I even tried chasing them away, but they weren't impressed, especially as they were much more nimble on their feet than I was. I soon became resigned to their presence and resolved to eat as much as possible between the end of work and the coming of the lorry. They really were the most unattractive of creatures. Where the wool should have been packed tightly and bounce as they walked, it hung in limp and lifeless stalactites, with the overall colour of a heavily laden stormcloud. The smell from them was pungent, and more reminiscent of goats.

'Why the hell do you have to come here?' I enquired of one of them.

'Nowt else,' was the short reply.

'What do you mean, 'nowt else? You must come from a farm somewhere?'

'No,' said the ewe.

'Where do you go when you get into that lorry, then?' I asked.

'Wait to come back here,' was the reply.

This was getting me nowhere, but it did present a challenge worth pursuing, such was the difficulty in prising information from any of them. I moved on and tried another.

'Why can't you eat your own grass?' I started.

'Cause there ain't none,' came the reply.

'I don't wonder at that, seeing how you all eat when you get here.'

'Don't be so damn rude,' she said, spitting bits of grass out as she spoke.

'Well, you must admit you go over this place like a broom in a stable yard.'

'Maybe, but it's not grass we lack, it's just that our gaffer hasn't got any land to grow it on. All we have is the common land at the top of the 'ill, here, and that's as bare as a baby's arse, and a tiny paddock by gaffer's caravan.' Before she had even finished the sentence her nose was on its way to the ground, in search of the next mouthful.

'Are there many of you, then?' But I was wasting my breath on her.

'Who's your owner?' I asked the next one I came to.

'What's it to you?'

'Sorry, just wondered, that's all,' I said apologetically.

'It's Bill, if you must know.' She didn't make me feel welcome.

'Is Bill local to here?' I asked of the next ewe.

'Our Bill, you mean?' I nodded. 'Bill Fraser, brother to Matt Fraser, your gaffer. Bloody hate each other's guts they do. Bill and his sister took your man to court and got him thrown out of the family home. Don't think your Matt'll ever get over that. They tell me he thinks the whole world's got it in for 'im.' She actually looked up to tell me all this, so I thought I would try and keep her talking.

'Why did they want the house?' I asked.

'Only to sell it, though Lord knows what they did with the money. Never bought any land for us, anyways.' She tossed her eyes heavenwards with this last phrase.

'How do you manage with so little land, then, or do you poach all the time?'

'There's many more of us, you know. Must be over a hundred sheep in all, more with the few lambs that survived. Then there's half a dozen goats, two ponies by the caravan, four mares and a stallion on the common land. Even a handful of cattle around now and then.'

'Good grief!' I exclaimed, 'What do you all live on?'

'Some of us do this by nights. There's a large group up on the common, or supposed to be.' She snatched at a piece of grass and went on, 'They'll have moved on by now. Bill cuts a hole in the wire fence. Just like a cat flap it is. The sheep all go through and then he lets it down again. You'd never see it if you didn't know where to look.'

'What about his horses?' I asked.

'They mostly stop on the top of the hill, but if things gets too bad they'll find a way out or he'll just open the gate and let them loose.' Before I could ask another question she had shuffled off with her face to the ground.

One morning, after the roaming flock had been in the field for the best part of the night, Glyn came out to feed me as he did if I was not going to work. After leaving me with a bowl of oats he took a walk round the field and I could see that his curiosity was aroused by the number of small droppings. Since these underfed sheep were also undersized, their droppings followed suit, and could easily have been mistaken for those of rabbits. This must have been Glyn's first reaction, for I could see him poking in the undergrowth near the edge of the field but I sensed he got to the truth of the matter before he left.

That night the sheep were duly delivered but, before they were collected the next morning, Glyn drove up in his battered Land Rover. He sat on the gate for a while contemplating his course of action and then, unwisely, set about trying to catch at least one of the culprits. This is not an easy task with any sheep, but these lean and alert ones would have proved an able match for the sharpest of Rugby players let alone a middle-aged, portly man, dressed in several layers of warm clothing, heavy trousers and wellingtons at least one size too large. His approach was at first a subtle one, walking nonchalantly towards his intended victim, and making an effort not to look directly at it. Then, when within striking distance, to lunge at it with both arms and his stubby fingers outstretched, in the hope of getting a grip on some part of the fleece. The ewes didn't even have the decency to take this effort seriously and continued to graze intently, while making the occasional short sprint to avoid what they must have though was man tripping over a tuft of grass.

Feeling that I could be of assistance in the matter I made an effort to join in by spotting which animal was to be singled out

next, and then endeavouring to cut off its line of retreat by positioning myself on the opposite side of it to Glyn. This tactic was no more successful than the last, for the sheep just shot out between us like a bar of wet soap. In fact, it would appear that at this stage I was getting a lot of blame for the failure of the plan, for after each unsuccessful attempt there would be a hail of missiles around me, ranging from handy clods of earth to large pieces of wood. I thought I would show how he might succeed, by getting them all into a bunch and then making a grab for one, once they were in a corner. To get this under way I set off round the field at a great pace, totally encircling the sheep. It only took me two circuits before the whole lot were huddled together in the middle. Now it was up to Glyn to see what I had in mind. This he must have done, for he slowly walked out to join me in the middle. As he did so, the ewes made a move away from him and I followed so as to ensure that they kept moving and stayed together. When the edge of the field was reached they halted, and turned to face us. Supposedly trapped between their pursuers and the boundary, Glyn closed in, while I waited to counter any escape bid. As he made his attack they darted out of his way. He just caught one with the outstretched fingers of his right hand. This was enough to commit him to a full rugby-style tackle, and whilst horizontal on the ground, the pull of the ewe turned him through ninety degrees. He landed facing the direction that the ewes had gone, and as he did so, he lost his precarious grip only to be left with a small piece of wool. Whilst this was happening I had foreseen the move the sheep would make, and had moved in the same direction to head them off. Not expecting to meet me as well, they turned as one, terrified of the thundering of my hooves, and bolted from whence they had come. Unfortunately I had moved so swiftly that Glyn had not had time to regain his feet and was still kneeling on the ground as the mob came upon him. Now in full flight from a monster that shook the ground with every move, they scarcely noticed his presence in front of them. By the time the last of them was clear of the area I could see Glyn, again lying prostrate in the mud. From that moment on the sheep were of secondary importance to him. Not only mud and sticks,

36

but all manner of abuse came my way as I was pursued round the field.

The ewes, of course, were highly amused to see that Glyn's fury had now turned on me, and it is probably just as well that I couldn't hear what they were saying above the din that marked my progress. Nevertheless, I was master of the situation and kept well out of range but just close enough to tempt him to try and reach me. Now and then I would pretend that my line of retreat had to be through the bunch of sheep, so that they scattered, mouthing foul language as I plunged amongst them. Finally, very red in the face and totally exhausted, Glyn left us in peace. As he did so Bill, who must have been watching the circus act, arrived with his lorry and the sheep clambered aboard with a keenness I had not witnessed before. They did not return for a long time after that episode. Every time Glyn passed by though, he would come into the field and have a walk round, checking for any droppings which suggested they might have returned.

Thus it was, when the sheep were put in again, it was only two days before they were spotted. The following morning the operation was mounted in earnest, with not only Glyn, but the Estate shepherd, his dog, and two other people as well, one of whom I saw to be Mark. Attached to the back of Glyn's Land Rover was the stock trailer I had come to Barrymore in. It was reversed up to the gate, which was partially opened so as to form a barrier between the hedge and the side of the trailer, whilst the other side was closed in by a portable hurdle that must have been brought along for the purpose. As soon as the dog came into the field the sheep formed into a bunch and were herded towards the gateway.

Having witnessed the ease with which these animals loaded into the lorry that collected them daily, I thought they would go straight into the trailer. Not at all. They were much more evasive than I had been, twisting, turning and trying to break out between those who were urging them towards it. In desperation the shepherd made his move and dived into the bunch. As they scattered, I could see that he had a strong hold on one of them. This poor animal was dragged into the trailer and tied to the far end of it, whilst the whole group were gathered up again and brought back for another attempt. Now they were confused, for there, right in front of them, was one of their number in the trailer. At first the plan started to work and they moved towards the ramp but, just as Glyn and the rest closed in behind them, so the truth dawned. For a moment it was difficult to tell what was happening. Sheep and men seemed to be upended in very direction, but when comparative calm returned three more of the sheep had been restrained and were bundled into the trailer, their handlers by now completely covered in mud. With four of them in captivity the back had to be shut on them. The exercise was repeated by bringing the group to the gate, trying to catch as many as possible whilst they were there, and bundling them in through the side door.

During the second manoeuvre the ewes' owner started calling his flock from somewhere up in the wood. Recognising him, they made every effort to escape their pursuers; some found ways through the hedge, others jumped over or pushed under the hurdle. The dog was by now delirious, trying to hold some in a group whilst also attemptingto stop every escape bid. The action of the dog, more than anything else, contributed to the few numbers that were ultimately caught, for he scattered them far and wide and chased many into the hedge at such a speed that they went straight through, to emerge tattered and dazed, but free on the other side. Eight were eventually caught when Matt, who had wisely kept away during this pantomime, came to take me to work.

I heard later that the ewes had been taken to the same stable where I had spent my first night at Barrymore. They had been padlocked in there until Bill Fraser had handed over a large sum of money to secure their release. The warmth of the stable and the ample supply of food had made it a pleasant stay for them, but the impounding of his stock had taught Bill not to try the same trick again on Barrymore, so there were no more lorry loads in the middle of the night, although I daresay some other farmer in the locality has unwittingly grazed them for a night or two.

The ewes were still around, though, for I met many of them

again through the winter months, mostly as they roamed the wood in search of food, rummaging under decaying leaves and heaps of pine needles for anything edible. Some would die of hunger and exposure, whilst quite a large number would succumb to the temptation to eat the succulent green branches of the Yew tree, only to die a rapid and painful death. Over the years Matt and I were to discover many of their carcasses lying in the woods.

4
GRAVITY AND TIMBER TAKE CONTROL

As you, the reader, have gathered, following Kit's death I stayed on at Barrymore as their tushing horse. Whether it had been intended from the start that I remain, I don't know, but I had no complaints about the arrangement. Over the next few years I was to become quite famous in the area. The incident I shall come to shortly was one reason—it probably saved Matt's legs, if not his life.

Barrymore Estate had three distinct areas of woodland. Moat Wood, which was by Cid's field; Farm Wood, which as the name implies was by the farm; and Oldhill Wood, which was by far the largest and where I lived and worked most of the time. There were four fields I could use, depending on where I was working at the time. The one I refer to as 'my field' was the most central, and therefore home, but at times I would be in with Cid or by the

40

farm, both of which I enjoyed as it meant I had the company of other horses. On this occasion I was based in Kit's field as the work happened to be on adjoining land.

Briefly, you could split my work into two distinct types. the most common was the dragging of small trees, known as thinnings, from where they had been felled. They were used either for fencing stakes or rails, and were called thinnings because they were taken from within a plantation in order to give more room to the trees left. Because there was very little space within which to work, the job was impracticable for a tractor or winch, neither of which could operate without damaging the trees that were to be left standing.

The other type of work, which ran from mid-October for two months, was the collecting of Christmas trees from within the plantations, and taking them out to the roadside for collection by other transport. For this a large sledge, akin to a metal bed-frame on stout runners, was towed behind me with the trees piled high on it.

However, one job turned out to be a bit different, as I was pulling rather larger pieces of timber than I had ever attempted to move previously. Some magnificent Larch trees, at least fifty years old, had been felled within a crop of young Redwood trees. In itself this had been a highly skilled operation, involving very careful felling of extremely large trees. Often the younger Redwoods had been tied out of the way, in order to make a gap where the Larch could fall. The problem remained, though, of getting the Larch to the edge of the wood from where it could be marketed. Some were readily accessible to a crawler and winch, but a great many would cause too much damage to the Redwood crop, from the machines and long wire ropes if this system was to be used.

It was then decided to try the ago-old system of a horse and chains, despite the size of the timber to be moved. To make it all possible the trees had been cut into smaller lengths but were still very heavy. The plan was for me to move the logs from where they fell, to a central track which had previously been cleared and from where the crawler could take over. Doing it this way I would only have to go down, or diagonally, across the hill. Both methods caused problems, although going across the hill was potentially the worse.

We started slowly with the smaller pieces. Even these I could not get to move by merely putting my weight against the chains, which is what I would normally have done to get them under way. On command I would move forward, until the chain had tightened around the log, then I would back up, get some slack and hope that the jolt, when it came taut again, would set us in motion. But this did not always work immediately and on occasions several angles of the pull had to be tried before we got going.

The toll on the chains and track was considerable and all parts under strain had to be replaced by stronger versions, otherwise over half the day was being wasted in waiting for repairs to be completed. It didn't take long though, with the strengthened tack, for us to get into the swing of the job. Matt had become more adept at where, and at what angle, to connect the chains. I, for my part, had become fitter and developed the knack of snatching at the log to get it moving. That we were so successful was obviously a surprise to all but Matt and myself. We had many spectators who would come and watch in amazement, as man and horse coped with timber which would have caused a small tractor to stop dead where it was.

My only regret was that Kit was not there to work with me. Being in her field I thought of her a lot, and how well we could have worked together on this particular job. What fun it might have been! The two of us putting our combined weight and strength into moving these enormous logs! With her constant pull and my strength, we could have safely moved much larger lengths. I pictured the two of us, harnessed to a really big log, hauling it across the contour of the hill, sap like golden syrup oozing from the wounds inflicted on its bark as we ruthlessly hauled it over the ground and cut into it with ropes and chains. Kit leaning into the harness and thrusting out with her massive hind quarters, whilst the muscles in her shoulders rippled beneath the large leather collar that transferred her pull to the chains and load behind. At the same time I would watch for the stumps, that by now were partially hidden beneath the flattened undergrowth, and then change the angle of pull as required. Once clear of the stumps and other trees our pull would be as one, straining stride for stride to get the timber to the road. We certainly could have been a famous pair! Foresters would have come from far and wide to witness such a spectacle.

I was still picturing the two of us, when I realised that Matt had finished for the day and we were on our way back to Kit's field, which was so close to the Larch and Redwood that we only had to walk twenty metres down the tarmac road to reach it.

As at Pen-y-Bont, this was the time of day for the big change-over, when the bold and cheerful creatures of the day would happily find a safe place to wait and sleep, until the misty light of dawn signalled them to start on their busy lives again, whilst their place was taken by the stealth and craft of the nocturnal ramblers and hunters. The first to pass my way was a badger. He shoved his way into the field using his broad shoulders to temporarily enlarge the gap in the hedge as if he were walking through a pair of swing doors. He knew precisely where he was going and kept up the same busy shuffle until he went out under the gate, diagonally opposite to where he had come in. I could see that he followed a well-worn path and wondered what was so important to him that he set off constantly in the same direction. The air was now feeling quite damp as the dew drifted off the higher parts of the hill and settled in the flat lands at its base. The badger had left a distinctive line behind him, where he had taken the dew off the grass as he passed.

'Ark!' This was loud and shrill, only a few metres from where I stood but over the hedge towards the wood. It gave me such a fright that my legs seemed to buckle under me, but with a lot of steps I swung round to face the direction from which the sound had come. Nothing. Not another sound. Not even the crackle of a leaf.

'Sorry about that. Didn't know you were here,' said a voice some two metres to my left. I turned, to see a small black nose poking through the same gap that the badger had used. Even in

43

the half light I could see that it was the fine muzzle of a fox. He came on into the open, making the hole seem big enough to drive a lorry through.

'Are you the horse from the other end of the wood?' he enquired, 'Come to take over from the old mare?'

'Yes, but I was here before . . .' I left it at that.

'That's right, I had heard you were both here for a bit.' Something caught his eye just to the right of him. He sniffed at it and rolled it over with his paw and then picked it up between his teeth. He was still trying to chew the slug between his molars when he added, 'She told me as a matter of fact. Took quite a fancy to you, she did.' I felt a flutter of excitement but said nothing.

'Yup, she used to talk to me a lot some evenings. Sometimes I had to go and do a bit of hunting and I'd leave her here talking away. I don't think she even noticed I had gone.'

'You must have been good friends,' I said.

'She knew she was going to die.' He rightly ignored my rhetorical question.

'Her main regret was that you only came here now. She had some crazy idea about the two of you working together on some big timber. Seemed to me you would be treading on each other's toes all the time.' He looked up to see the distant expression in my eyes. 'Yes, well, all of us here in Oldhill were very attached to her, you know.' He could see it was going to be difficult for me to get any words out for a bit. 'I'll be off now. See what's been left around the pub over there. Maybe have a word with you on my way back. Bye'. He trotted off after the badger, leaving only little pad marks behind him to mark his progress. I must have been asleep when he came past on his way home, for I didn't see him again that night.

I awoke with the brightness of the morning. The dew was still thick on the ground and shone as it caught the bright rays of the sun. Between some of the taller grasses and in the hedges, the cobwebs had also collected the dew. The intricate patterns sparkled as they moved back and forth in an undetectable breeze, suspended on fine, elasticated threads. As I went down the road

44

alongside Matt, the breath curled out of my nostrils in two distinct spirals, but the sun was already warm on my back. When we turned into the wood it was chill and damp, only in the clearing were we tempted to stand still and catch the sun's rays.

Viewed from afar it appeared as though the wood was set on uniformly sloping ground, but once inside, the true undulations could be seen. It is the natural growth of the trees that produces an even covering, for in their struggle to get a share of the light the ones on the lower slopes push harder and faster for the sky. Now, however, the differences were more marked, for the valleys still had a veil of mist lying in them, making it look as if the trees below were growing out of cotton wool.

It was on one of these particularly steep slopes that we were to work that day, still pulling the heavy logs around the contours as best we could. It was never easy but today it was particularly difficult. Ideally, I would follow a line around the hill until I came to the track where the timber was to be left, but often there were obstructions on the line that had to be avoided. It could be a stump from one of the large Larches, a Redwood that had been left to grow on, or even the holes of foxes, rabbits and badgers, all of which I had to get around.

Due to the weight of the tow it was virtually impossible to turn uphill to get by these obstructions, so that for each deviation I came further down, which in turn meant that it was longer around the contour of the hill to reach my destination. Unwisely, on rare occasions I would try to head uphill if a clear passage on the lower side was not immediately apparent.

On one such occasion I had forgotten the enormity of the particular log I had behind me. It was perfectly straight, and over two feet in diameter at the larger of the two ends, without any blemishes where branches had been removed for it had come from the section of tree where they had been pruned, about twenty-five years previously, to give just such a high quality timber. Ahead of me was not one of the normal obstacles I have already mentioned, but a more unusual one and just as effective in barring the way. There were a lot of these any heaps throughout the wood, but it was not often that they became an obstacle as this one had. The ants themselves were encouraged, because they climbed the trees and ate the parasites on them. Rumour had it that these particular monsters in Oldhill Wood, which were amongst the largest ants I had ever seen, had been deliberately imported from Canada. Directly to the lower side of the anthill was a collection of young Redwoods and just below them, there was a small amount of earth that was still damp from when it had been dug out by rabbits the night before. I didn't want to come to a halt so that I would have to get the log on the move again, so, putting on a bit of a sprint, I endeavoured to go to the top side. Once before I had tried to drag a log through one of these heaps but, being a metre high and over three around the base, it acted like a pile of loose sand and, although disfigured, impeded further progress most effectively.

The leading end of the log had drawn level with the ant heap when the butt end, which was the larger and therefore heavier, started to roll. As it did so it pivoted about its middle, so that the butt was pointing further downhill, while I had been moved back-wards by its force. At the same time it had been rolling, twisting the chains between us. Now it was starting to gather momentum, half sliding, half rolling down the hill and into the valley below. Being still attached to it I was having to execute a sort of running half-pass trying to stay on my feet and keep up with the log, while moving by crossing my nearside legs over and behind my offside ones. Not easy to do at speed. It also occurred to me that soon the speed would be such that I could no longer keep up with the projectile, in which case I would be dragged bodily to the bottom or, alternatively, a tree would come between us, the consequence of which I chose not to try and imagine.

I jumped as best I could to my right, and in doing so gained a small amount of slack line so that if I moved fast I would be facing the same way as the log. Then my speed increased, until I was overtaking it. The noise was quite frightening, as the pair of us hurtled down the wood. the ground behind us looked level after our passing as all weeds, bushes and pine needles were swept up and taken with us. By now I was in a strong canter, and trying hard to gain enough lead not only to tighten the chain, but to bring what had become a pendulum into line, astern of me. On, down the slope we went, so fast that I scarcely had time to see where my feet might land with each new stride. How would I ever stop? Would the ground ever level out, or did it end in a ravine? I really had no idea, since this was not a part of the wood that I had been to previously.

A split second before we were on it, I saw the track. It was to join us at about forty-five degrees, and although it was still down-hill, the slope was less and, mercifully, clear of obstacles. Getting onto it was not so easy, for it had been cut into the hillside, leaving a substantial bank near vertical in inclination, to be negotiated on the side from which we had now approached. There was no time for decision making. As I reached the edge I jumped. The chains to the log behind me were tight, so much of the spring was taken out of my leap. Instead of clearing the bank and landing on the track as I intended, I was suspended momentarily in mid-air, only to descend with my fore feet on the track, my hind feet halfway up the cutting. At the moment of landing. the timber behind me came over the edge and struck me a mighty blow on my quarters. Meanwhile, the log, having been slightly checked by hitting me, nose-dived onto the track and buried its finer end deep into a muddy wheel rut. I completed a neat roll and ended up lying at right angles to the log. Scrambling to my feet I made to get away from the scene as soon as possible, only to find that I was very firmly anchored by the chain, which was still round the log. To make matters worse, I could see the log and the chain both going out of sight beneath the earth, as it was to the narrower end that my chain was attached. After the noise of our descent the ensuing silence seemed as if everything, including the breeze in the trees, had stopped, to try and discover what had been happening. The loudest sound was my heart beat, which thumped in my ears until I felt sure it must have been audible to those around me in the wood. I could just feel my legs shaking beneath me, although they also had a numbness about them, such as only happens after a bout of extreme exertion. Of Matt, there was no sign. He had been behind me at the top of the hill before the whole episode had started for now I had stopped, I could recall him shouting 'Whoa!' as the log had commenced to roll. Whether it was directed at the log or myself must be in doubt, although the two of us were even then firmly committed to the sleigh run.

It was probably due to to my still-pounding heart but I did not hear Matt, until he jumped down onto the track beside me. I was so relieved to see him that I whinned. Not a normal thing for me to do, unless directed towards other horses. His immediate reaction was to try and release me, but this would not prove to be a simple task. He made a futile attempt to pull the log back out of the ground and then dug down with his bare hands in an effort to reach the point at which I was attached, both of which ended in failure. An attempt to detach the chain from my harness was equally unsuccessful, as due to the twisting action of the timber the shackle was now under such tension that it could not be undone. He left again, leaving me shackled like a convict.

When he returned, Glyn had joined him. They stood on the bank for some time while Glyn was convulsed with laughter at what had happened, but when he came down to my level he soon removed all my tack, leaving it still connected to the other end, but mercifully letting me go. Whilst Matt walked me gently up the hill, a tractor was brought to the scene to remove the offending timber and salvage my harness.

The rest of the working day must have been dull by comparison, for I cannot remember any of it. It was back in the field and nearly dusk when the first comment on the events earlier in the day was made.

'I have been awake most of the day thanks to the noise you made.' The voice came from the skeleton-like remains of a dead elm tree in the hedgerow. 'You wouldn't have noticed, at the speed you were going, but a lot of us night workers had a disturbed morning.' There, where one of the bald boughs met the trunk of the tree, sat a bundle of fluff with a pair of dark eyes set on top of it.

'It wasn't my choice to go down there, you know.'

'Should think not,' said the owl. 'You're damn lucky.' He went on, 'I was sat about two-thirds of the way up one of those little Redwoods when you came by. Twigs, dust, stones, pine needles. There were all sorts of things flying round in your wake. That log

48

wasn't even straight out behind you, but rolling across the slope, or it was until it came to my tree. That straightened it out all right! Trouble was the shock, when it hit. Sent me flying, literally!' The thought of it made him shuffle and reorganise his wings.

'I can guarantee you won't be disturbed like that in the future.' I meant it. 'The shock of it has yet to wear off but, when it does, the memory will linger on for a very long time.'

'Doesn't suit me having to move in the middle of the day like that.' He looked at me wearily. 'At night I do what I like around here, even eat the odd sparrow or two, but during the day they all gang up on me and give me a rough time. That's why I normally choose a good spot and stay put from dawn till dusk. They never see me then; too busy rushing about, twittering to each other to notice anything that keeps still.'

For many, it was now time to find their respective resting places, and there was a lot of activity in the air all around us. Blackbirds were shrieking as they darted from hedge to bush and back again, whilst overhead the crows had gathered into groups and were also holding a noisy discussion on where and when to settle. All this and more was seen by the owl. His lethargic blinks belied his alert mind, of which his rapid head movements gave a much better indication.

Whilst I had been so involved in watching this strange bird, I had failed to notice the rabbit that had hopped up alongside me.

'My ceiling fell in on me today,' she complained.

'I've already told this owl that what happened was not deliberate.' I swung my head in the direct of the dead elm tree.

'Frightened my family silly, it did. My old buck, Fred, didn't seem to care, but the rest of us, well it scared us rigid. It was really scary, I tell you.'

'You don't need to tell me, my friend.' A touch of sarcasm crept into my voice. 'If it was frightening underground in your cosy little home, you should try being on the end of a log!' Dropping my voice slightly I added, 'Pity you weren't . . .'

'There is no need to get nasty about it,' she snapped, 'I didn't really come to complain. It's not that bad. We have got to dig out a lot of the burrow again, but it's only loose earth to get out this time.'

'Sorry.' I felt a bit mean.

'Of course, the children think the whole burrow is spooked now. They want us to go and find a new spot to live. They will get over it in time though, I hope.' The rabbit raised her brow and sighed as she finished.

'I hope it doesn't affect them too much.' I said.

'Oh, probably not, although they won't even come out at the moment, convinced that there must be a vast demon above ground waiting to crush them with his big feet as soon as they appear.'

Had I been able to get out of the field as and when I liked, this last statement of hers could well have been true for I was starting to feel that I could cheerfully do it to her, in addition to all her off-spring. I walked away, trying hard to ignore the continuing saga of the rabbit family, which went on quite well despite the lack of any reply from me. Why was it that these animals should have come out of their way to complain to me about something over which I had no control? In all probability I would never see either of them again. I certainly didn't recall having met them previously.

'You certainly stirred things up this morning, didn't you?' The fox's nose was pushing through the hedge again.'

'Not you, as well! What harm did I cause you?' I asked as he came on into the field.

'None. Best thing that's happened to me for a long time,' he replied.

'I don't see how that can be, but it certainly makes a change from all the complaints that seem to be coming my way this evening.' He had already cheered me up considerably.

'Well, I can tell you, I haven't found a meal with such ease since they had the barbecue over at the big house and I cleared up after them! When you finished work I went down that swathe left behind after your performance, digging out all the mouse nests that you partly exposed.' He licked his lips at the memory.

'It's just as well that it is too far for them to walk, or that would be the biggest complaint of the whole lot – from those that survived, anyway.' Despite the disaster that had befallen the mice, I still felt better than before his arrival.

'Thanks to you I don't have to hunt tonight, so I am going to go for a wander around, have a word with some of my mates over in Moat Wood. See if there are any vixens over there that I might court, later in the winter.' He pulled himself up to his full height and shook out his bushy tail.

'If you see Cid over there, give him my regards and tell him what happened today. It would amuse him,' I requested.

'That's the least I can do for you, after today,' he replied. With that he set off across the field with a bounce to his stride.

It was to be a restless night, as seemingly the whole population of the wood came at one time or another, to talk about the previous day's event. When I did get to sleep it was only to relive the whole episode over again. It was just as well that Matt and I couldn't converse, for then the subject would almost certainly have gone through the next day as well. Instead, it was a relief to get away and back into harness, although the day was to prove to be another eventful one. In complete contrast to the day before, we were now put to work on the most level piece of wood that there was within the Larch and Redwood. Nevertheless, I had a sneaking suspicion that, once the memory had dulled a bit with time, we would have to go back and finish the steep slope.

The work was just as hard but we got going well as the day wore on, moving more logs since the pull was more direct, not having to follow around any contours. Matt would back me up to the end of the timber, attached the chains then stand back as I tightened them, backed up once more, and snatched them away. Since it was easier to keep them moving if a brisk pace was kept up, Matt would run alongside until we got to the stack then, once I had backed up to give him a slack line, he would detach me before we set off back up the wood to start the process all over again. It would be impossible for me to say how many logs we had moved by mid-afternoon, but the next one did not appear any different from the others. It had been coupled to the chains and we were under way when I felt a jolt as it made contact with something solid on the ground. Without stopping I looked back, to see what it had hit, and saw a newly-exposed tree stump that my feet must have only just missed. Worse still, though, the log I had in tow was now running along another which we had yet to move. As it slithered along, slightly at an angle, it collected Matt at knee level. He was knocked over backwards by its great weight and pace. As he fell his back came up against one of the trees that had not been sawn down, so that he was left sitting with his back to the tree. As he reached the ground he let out the by now familiar 'Whoa!'. I had already done so, but the log would only stop when it had lost all its forward momentum. This took a surprisingly long time because it was not in contact with the ground over much of its length, as it was pivoting on the other log as it slid along. It probably would have gone on moving longer still had it not come into contact with Matt first, for it had found a resting place on his lap.

It was obvious that he was in considerable pain, but I couldn't see at first that there was anything I could do to help him get out of the situation. When I started to turn around very carefully, lest I should move the log at all, Matt cried out for me to stay, so I instantly stopped where I was. Clearly though, this wasn't the right answer for we could have both remained as we were for at least another three hours, before it would be noticed that Matt had not returned from the wood. I started to move again. Once more Matt shouted at me to stop. This time, however, I kept going so that I turned to face him and the timber in his lap. I had become quite skilful over the years at placing timber in stacks, unaided. The situation did not occur often but, now and then, I would work between two men, one who was felling timber and the other making the stakes. When one of them had finished cutting all the branches off a felled tree he would harness me to it and send me off. I would find my own way down through the wood to the stack of timber that I was making, and when I had got the log correctly in line with all the others I would wait for the other man to come and disconnect me. When he had done that and put the chains over my back, I returned to the tree feller for the next load. Many times I could approach the middle of the stack from the uphill side and, by picking my way over a few of the logs, I could swing the one I had in tow so that it came to rest on top and perfectly in line with the others already there. With the aid of this knowledge I could now see how, if I were to be extremely careful, I could remove the timber from Matt. Amid loud shouts from him, imploring me to stand still, I started to move away from him to position myself on the other side of the log which had caused the problem in the first place. It was my intention to take up the strain from the far side so that the log to which I was attached and which had so securely pinned down Matt, would reverse the course it had taken earlier and slide back up the other tree, at the same time being lifted clear of its victim. When I had reached the intended angle I slowly let the chain tighten before applying any real pull. By this time Matt had seen what I was endeavouring to do, and remained transfixed and amazed, in complete silence. I only hoped my plan would be a success.

As the pull increased, the log appeared to be rolling over rather than moving with me. The sounds from beneath the tree must have been for me to stop, although they were not familiar to me, but their tone indicated pain. What was happening was inevitable, because when I had been pulling the timber the joining link had been on the near side of the log; now that I had crossed to exert a pull from the offside, the first movement had to be the log rolling over before any lateral movement could commence. I kept on pulling and, sure enough, the log first lifted clear and then slid back up the tree as I had planned. Matt rose to his feet and leant heavily against the tree, whilst I kept the tension on the chain in case the log should return to its former position if I let it go. It was some time before he was able to move his limbs freely and abandon the support of the tree, but as soon as he had done so I let the weight take me back, and sure enough the timber returned to its former position abutting the tree, but thankfully without Matt as the meat in the sandwich.

I was uncoupled and given a pat, then the pair of us made our way very slowly out of the wood, badly shaken for the second day in succession, although I glowed with pride at what I had done and the comradeship from the pat.

Following these two events the rest of the timber was duly cleared from the area without incident. It took a long time, and it was well into the winter months before we had finished and I had returned to the field.

After only two nights back 'home', there was a strong gale. The wind had started in the afternoon. Thin wisps of cloud had begun to cross the sky, eventually forming into a complete haze and giving the impression of a halo round the sun. This halo gave way to ever darker and lower cloud, whilst the wind steadily increased in ferocity. By dusk the cloud was dense and fast moving, and under the solid mass were more little clouds scurrying on their way at even greater speed, urgently carrying the message of what was to come. By nightfall there was a true gale blowing, so strong was it that I found it difficult to know where to stand for the best. Under the shelter of the trees there was the risk of having limbs falling on one, but in the open it was cold and uncomfortable, in addition to needing constant muscular effort to counteract the ever-changing gusts. While the hardwood trees waved their boughs in the wind, the conifers gave to each gust with the whole of the trunk bending over, until the very tip was bent horizontal in the fiercest of these. There was a continous 'whoosh' from the wind through the wood, and then a similar but more urgent sound, as another fierce gust would come tearing through. The trees would bend further over, occasionally letting branches get carried off to crash into the next tree downwind of them. With the sound heralding the arrival of a gust, there would sometimes come a sharp crack, signalling the breaking of a trunk under the great strain imposed on it by the resistance to the wind of its bushy crown. When these tops broke away they did so in the vertical position, before they had had a chance to bend and give to the power of the wind. They were then carried downhill in an upright attitude, looking absurd for a while prior to falling or, more usually, smashing into another tree. The stronger gusts ceased after two hours and the wind died away slowly, so that by dawn, peace had returned to let the world see the chaos that had been left in the wake of the storm.

I was collected as usual and returned once more to the Redwood, the Larch having all been removed. What a sad sight greeted us both. After all the care and attention that had been

54

taken to protect these trees during the extraction of their nurse crop, it brought a feeling of nausea to look on the scene that was now before my eyes. In place of the clearings we had made, lay twisted and tangled Redwoods. More used to the shelter given by the older trees they had failed to develop sufficient strength in their trunks or root systems, to withstand such a gale.

The Christmas tree season would be upon us again by the time Matt and I were to finish in this part of Oldhill Wood.

5
ESCAPE, FREEDOM AND FRIENDS

For me at least, the Christmas tree season started with a little bit of a break, as before there were any trees to haul out of the woods, all the men, including Matt, had to go in with spades and picks to dig them up. It was only later that I became involved. This year I was given advance warning before that I was due to start, for I was stood at the top of my field when I heard the distinctive sound of Glyn's Land Rover. This vehicle worked every bit as hard as I did, nearly all of its life being spent off the hard road and on woodland tracks, which resulted in it sounding laden at all times due to the weight of mud that clung to it. Also it always seemed to be struggling for breath; the reason for this was plain for all to see, as the exhaust pipe was almost entirely flattened through persistent bottoming over stumps and deeply rutted tracks.

On this particular ocassion it was coming down the public road that ran across one end of my field, more heavily laden than ever. Strapped to it, piggy-back style, with one end resting against the tail gate and the other well up in the air over the cab roof, was my sledge. Predictably, Glyn duly delivered Matt to my field the next morning; the harness was fitted and off we both went, with Matt on my back, to the relevant part of the wood. The last time I had been to this area of Oldhill Wood it had been filled with a crop of forty-year-old Larch trees but, since then, the whole thirty acres had been cleared and in its place were thousands of little Christmas trees, all in rows extending relentlessly on into the distance, marching up and down the banks of the streams without ever breaking rank. Their militaristic manner was only spoilt by the obvious lack of organised growth, for in that they varied to a large degree. Some were in the form of small, tight bushes, more reminiscent of plants in a garden border, while at the other extreme, there were tall, spindly specimens, almost totally devoid of side branches and struggling skywards with a weak and wavering arm. These types appeared to dominate, for those that did not stand out through their blemishes or peculiarities lay slain on the battlefield, like so many nameless soldiers, awaiting the arrival of my sledge upon which they would be thrown to start their final journey.

The entire patch gave the impression of having been sliced out of the rest of the wood. On three sides there were still large trees, and it appeared that the cut had been made so accurately that even the trees on the boundary were devoid of branches on their outer edges. Bisecting it like a ragged scar, was the track to which all the Christmas trees would be brought for grading and tying into bunches. To the left of this path and a little over halfway along it, stood a solitary tree. It must either have been left in error or as a monument to the previous crop, but as the sole survivor of an era past it now presented a sad sight. Leaning at a precarious angle away from the prevailing wind, it was now nearly devoid of branches. Those that remained were on the leeward side and reached for the ground, as if in an effort to break the inevitable fall.

The work was dull and tedious. Most of the day I would stand motionless as trees were loaded onto the sleigh. I worked by voice command only on these occasions, as Matt would help the others. Each time we reached the hard track I would halt, whilst the trees were thrown into various heaps depending on their size. As soon as the sledge was empty we would return to the bottom of the row and start the process again. As I stopped, the men would start to load and once all the trees had been gathered from within easy reach, a shout would tell me to move on and the cycle would begin all over again. For something to break the monotony, I would try and anticipate the order to move on by watching to see when there were no more trees. This would work well, until I made a mistake. Then there would be a lot of shouting, as not only Matt but everyone else tried to stop me instantly. The worst mistake of all was to move off when there was someone adjusting the trees at the top of the load, for it appeared to be impossible for them to remain standing in these circumstances. If they were lucky and stood towards the front of the load, they fell within its confines, but if at the back or near side, a fall to the ground was inevitable. In these latter circumstances I had found it best to get away from my victim, who by now would be brandishing some sort of weapon with which to castigate me. As he advanced, so I would start to walk. When his pace increased I would do likewise, until he was running but still not gaining on me. At this point the fear of losing the trees already loaded would be paramount in his mind. The weapon thrown away, he would make to clutch at the sleigh to steady it, which I would take as the signal to stop, for at this point I knew from experience that the relief of not losing the load would exceed the anger that had preceded it.

The work went on relentlessly. To actually see that we were really making progress towards the other end of the track you would have had to have marked off the rows day by day. Each was the same as the last, and the distance from one end of the track to the other never seemed to alter. Ahead of us there was a gang still digging more and more trees, followed by those who were tying them into bundles. No one seemed happy with the work, and very few words passed between the men. When those ahead of us digging, changed to tying behind, the end was in sight, and then suddenly it arrived. The last few rows disappeared rapidly, and I gratefully returned to the field.

The next day the sledge went by again, in the opposite direction, but once more riding piggy-back on the battered Land

Rover, which left a strong odour of the hot baked mud on its exhaust. I was very surprised to see it return shortly afterwards without the load on its back, but carying a passenger who I had never seen before. The two men came through the gate and up the field towards me. The man with Glyn was much taller than him, wore a peaked cap under which showed two shifty eyes, and his face seemed to have a fixed grin on it. Like many of the men, he wore blue overalls, but over them he wore what was obviously the jacket to a very smart suit. No wellingtons but a pair of reddish-coloured work boots, with bright yellow laces adorned his feet. I was caught by Glyn and tied with baling twine that was passed through my head collar and back to the barbed-wire fence. My harness was then put on by Glyn, who immediately removed it again and waited for the stranger to try his hand at the same task. Although there were many parts to the harness it had been on my back so many times that whenever it was put on, it seemed to fall into place. As soon as it came into contact with me I felt as if it had never been off, despite the hardness of the materials from which it was made. The collar around my neck was of thick leather, stuffed tightly with straw, while on either side of me and over my back went several sets of chains. This time proved to be the exception. Nothing felt as if it belonged and it was not until I had had a good shake that it all fell into place.

The baling twine was untangled from the barbed wire and we went out through the gate. Glyn got back into the Land Rover and departed, leaving the stranger and I to turn left, and left again into a lane that hitherto I had never been on. Up and up we walked. Oldhill Wood fell away behind and the road we were on turned into a gravel track. As we got higher, the vegetation turned from green to pale brown, with only the occasional flecks of a very dark green. We walked at a brisk pace, my new handler making no attempt to get on my back to ride to our destination. Presently, the climbing came to an end and unfolding in front of us was the most magnificent view. The brown of the dead bracken and the green of the gorse soon gave way to a bright green, as the hill fell away into a neat and tidy valley. Winding along the bottom was a country lane, flanked for its entire length by tall hedges.

59

Periodically there was a collection of grey stone buildings, showing where small holdings were sited. Beyond the valley, for our side was higher, enabling us to see out, there were more and more hills stretching out into the distance. The more distant they became the more they merged into the clouds, until both had taken on the same shade of grey, tinted with purple, that made it impossible to differentiate between the two. Instinctively I felt that those were the hills of my youth. They seemed to call out to me with haunting voice, imploring my return to their bleak and austere wilderness. I felt a sudden longing to be back there, independent and responsible for my own survival.

We never actualy dropped down into the valley itself but followed the track, which had become the dividing line between the fertile and the barren. On our left lay the scorched brown, whilst to the right there were fields divided by the same grey stone used for the houses lower down and containing the same sort of long-woolled sheep that had entered my field several months back. All the time we were travelling anti-clockwise around the hill, and I felt that we must soon be nearly opposite Oldhill Wood. The land to our right was now planted with trees, small ones that gave the appearance of having to fight hard for their existence. Then, to my horror, there were rows upon rows of Christmas trees. Not only that, but just inside the gate to the plantation was my sledge. It seemed that my toil was not over. We went through the gate and stopped in front of it. I backed up, waiting for the harness to be attached. The ground here was much more uneven than anything I had experienced before with the sledge, which made it difficult to move it smoothly. I was always led, never allowed to move in any direction of my own accord. This had the effect of making what was already an extremely boring job, even worse. To alleviate this I became very obtuse, and watched with satisfaction as the annoyance I was causing spread to those working with me. The last straw came when I was led straight over a large stump. Determined to do precisely as I was instructed, my feet slithering and slipping for want of grip, I made it to the other side and then had the satisfaction of watching the sledge gently roll over onto its side as one runner only mounted the stump.

Seeing the danger at the last second, the man at my head let go to try and support the load before it fell. Thus I had not been told to stop, so on I went dragging the sledge on its side and spreading the remains of the load over as large an area as possible. By the time they caught up and brought me to a halt, tempers were frayed. From the shouting and gesticulations I could tell that each was blaming the other for what had happened.

When the clamour subsided, to my relief I was uncoupled from the chaos behind and led away to a tiny enclosure, boggy under-foot and growing a crop of marsh reeds interspersed with tufts of couch grass. To keep the prisoners within its clutches were the remains of one of the popular stone walls, although this one had succumbed to the pressures of the weather and, I suspect, the patter of sheep feet, so that in parts it had been reduced to little more than a heap of grey rubble. The saving grace was the view. To the west could be seen the Welsh mountains that had so caught my eye earlier in the day. I stood transfixed by their mysterious beauty. Now and then I broke away to scour the field for something succulent, but found little that wasn't coarse or bitter, only to return to my westward-facing stance. Even after sunset, the shapes in the far distance could be seen silhouetted against the sky and the clouds. The latter changed from black to grey, depending on whether the moon was obscured or not at the time.

My thoughts and the relative calm of the night were interrupted when I heard the sound of horses grazing in the young plantation that adjoined my temporary abode. Straining to see in the poor light and through the broken lines made by the small trees, it was easy to imagine the outline of horses, but it was a long time before the image I had chosen coincided with the sound. There appeared to be a group of five, well spaced out, each following his or her line which led from one edible morsel to the next. I watched them for a long time as they ate their way further towards me. Since they hardly raised a head more than a few inches from the ground, they never became aware of my presence—not as long as I remained still—but I knew that I only had to take one stride on the squelching land for them to instantly know where I was. They had got very close to the dividing wall when I finally trotted towards them. As one, all five turned without looking in my direction, and fled for fifty metres or more where, in a bunch now, they looked back. One of them detached himself from the group and took a stride in my direction, snorting defiantly as he came to attention. I replied with a similar move and the process continued, until we were close enough to each to make physical contact. Whilst this had been going on between us, the remainder of his herd had been following at a safe distance. Now he was so close I knew him to be a stallion, but his manner had seemed to indicate that he would not be unduly protective of his mares. Even though we were now in contact he made no attempt to turn his hindquarters to kick, and although he stamped his forefeet on the ground, it was more by way of habit than a sign of true aggression. Gradually, the tension subsided and he allowed his mares to join him in looking over the wall at the stranger on their illegal grazing grounds.

'Would you be the Welsh horse Martha was telling me about?' asked the stallion.

'It's not very likely,' I replied, 'since I don't know this Martha.'

'Can't be from around here if you don't know Martha!' He addressed this to the mares as much as to me.

'Who is this Martha, then?' I asked, of no one in particular.

'Just one of my Guvnor's ewes,' said the stallion. 'But she talks a lot—well, a lot compared to the rest.'

'The only one that isn't downright rude,' came a voice from the back.

I knew who they meant now, although I had somehow never got to know the names of those sheep. I also knew that these were the mares and stallion to whom Martha had referred. I confirmed who I was and, feeling that perhaps I ought to pay more attention to names in future, introduced myself.

'Nice to meet you, Norman,' replied the stallion, sounding as if he really meant it. I couldn't help wondering what the ewe could have said about me to make him so welcoming.

'. . . right at the back is Wold.' He finished the introductions.

'I, er . . . sorry, but I'm not very good with names. Do you think you could . . . can you go through them again, please?' I wondered if, even in the half light, they could have seen that I hadn't been listening.

'Again then. I am Dean. On my right is Hereford. To the left is Abergavenny. Behind her is Stow, and right at the back is Wold.' He finished for a second time.

'Hi!' I said aloud, whilst to myself . . . Dean, Wold, Stow, Abergavenny and . . . and . . . 'We're all called after where we came from, you see,' said the mare to the right of Dean. To the right of him. That would be on his left as he looked at me, so that must be Abergavenny.

'That's how I got my name, you see. Hereford came from the market there and the other two came from Stow fair at Stow-on-the-Wold, but we couldn't call them both Stow, so we ended up with one of each. Dean didn't come from a market, but Bill Fraser, our guv'nor, bought him from a mate of his in the Forest −Forest of Dean, that is, so that's how he got his name.' Abergavenny finished her supplementary introductions.

'How about you?' asked Hereford. 'How did you get your name?'

'I don't know, I'm afraid. I've always been Norman−as long as I can remember.'

'Are you going to stay this side of the hill for long?' This came from Dean again.

'I hope not,' I replied. 'Just the half day I've been here already is too long! There's nothing to eat, the work is boring and in fact the only good thing is the view.'

'As much food as you want over the other side, I suppose,' Dean sounded envious.

'Oh no, not really.' I didn't want to give the impression that I was unduly coddled by humans. 'But certainly more than this small patch has to offer.'

They all exchanged knowing glances in what I felt was a well-rehearsed routine whenever they met up with more domesticated horses than themselves.

'If it is so bad, why do you stay?' It was Hereford's question this time.

'Yes, why don't you come with us?' added Abergavenny.

'The view is even better from the top of the hill,' Stow or Wold chipped in from the back.

'Why do you like the view, anyway?' asked Dean, whilst I was still wondering what I should answer to the first question.

'Mostly, because I haven't seen a view like that since I left Wales,' but it would be difficult to give them a full answer. I paused, then continued, 'When I came round the side of the hill earlier today the hills over there seemed to be beckoning to me. I felt an urge to return to the place of my youth. It almost felt as if I could leave here and miraculously find a path that would lead me all the way to a predetermined destination, high up on those hills.' My audience seemed to expect more so I went on, 'There was an otter I met in Wales, near to Welshpool and the River Severn, who told me that fish had very much that sort of instinct. They could leave the place of their birth, swim all the way across an ocean and then, three, four or five years later, come all the way back, and go up the same river again. Well, it could be that a bit of that same instinct is in all of us, couldn't it?'

'I tell you what,' Abergavenny broke the silence that followed. 'I think you have spent too much time with those humans and it's about time you had a bit of a break. So, get the hell out of that field and come with us!'

The thought of it was beginning to appeal. After all, if I stayed there was nothing more sure than that tomorrow morning I would be tacked up and backed into that wretched sledge which, at the moment, was still lying on its side with the disarray of all those trees around it. In fact, it would be more than likely that the men would have patched up their differences or, even worse, been told by Matt or Glyn that most of their problems of the previous day were of my making. Whichever way I looked at it, the future was not good.

'I'm shut in here, you know,' I said, stalling for time since an answer had obviously been expected.

'The ewes wander in and out of there without any trouble, so I'm sure you can,' said Hereford, making me wish I hadn't said anything at all. It had got to the stage where I either had to decline the offer and change the subject, or else make a move to get over the wall. I very much wanted the friendship and company, if only for a few days, and also knew that if I didn't go with them I would fall so much in their estimation that I may well not have the chance of meeting up with them again.

'Where do the ewes get over the wall?' I asked.

'You're coming then?' Dean seemed surprised at my decision.

'Yes, of course, but where do I get out?' I tried to disguise the fact that there had ever been any doubt in my mind but it must have been very obvious, for even my last question was unnecessary, since it was perfectly clear that any spot where the wall had fallen would suffice. Without waiting for a reply I turned and followed the outline of the stones until I came upon the first breach. As I looked up, having picked my way over the loose mound, Abergavenny was there to greet me.

'Welcome to a wild herd,' was her greeting.

'Where are we going to?' I asked, feeling that now I was free we should be making a run for it.

'We'll just stay around here awhile.' Dean had come over to join us.

'Look, now I'm out, I don't want to hang around waiting to be caught. Can't we clear off and get up on the top of the hill, far away?' It didn't seem right to break out and then remain grazing just the other side of the wall.

'They will expect you to go straight up to the common land on the hill. Everybody knows we are up there, and that will be the first place to be searched. No, let's stay here until we have all had plenty to eat, then we will go and lie up in the woods.' Dean seemed to have it all worked out in advance. As dawn broke we all made our way towards some young Larch trees. Now it was light, I could see what my new companions looked like. Dean was a very dark bay, with a thick neck and long, unruly mane. They all had tails down to the ground, but none had the same sort of mane and crest as Dean. Hereford was also a bay, that is brown, with a black mane and tail, as opposed to Dean, who seemed almost black all over. Abergavenny was a grey, a bit finer than the rest and with dark flecks in her mane and tail, while Stow and Wold were the smallest of the group, ponies really, but well built and both palominos, creamy with white blazes running down their muzzles.

'Split up and make for the hill for a while,' said Dean. 'Then pick your own line across the wood and we will regroup again in a clearing near the end of this patch. You will find it all right, Norman, and that should throw them off our trail for a while.' This was beginning to feel a bit more exciting, more as I had imagined it would be like to be out and on the run. I worked up through the wood, all the time heading for the clear light that I could see shining through the trees, which meant the end of the Larch plantation and the start of the common. When I got to the fence at the top I followed it along, in the same way as the wall around the field, until it was low enough to step over. At that point I hopped out and returned the way I had just come, but on the outside of the wood. I stayed on the outside until I found another low point in the fence line, where I got back over and set off in the direction I though the clearing would be. It wasn't difficult to find and the others were all there when I arrived.

'This is a bit open here but if you follow me through these trees we will come to an old quarry.' As Dean spoke he turned, and pushed in between the branches.

'You have clearly had to do this before,' I said, as we all started to pick our way behind him.

'Lots of times,' said Hereford, who had squeezed between Dean and myself as we started. 'Never ever been found down here, and we have had to use it whenever the food has got a bit low on the top of the hill. The locals see that we have been out eating the crops and trees, so they try to catch us in the daytime, which is why we hide here.' No wonder nobody ever found them. One second there were two horses in front of me, then nothing! It was as if the ground had swallowed them up which is, in effect, just what had happened. At first it looked as if there was a patch of small hardwood bushes in the midst of the Larch but, in reality, these were only around the edge of the quarry although they had grown towards the hollow centre, making use of all the available light and hanging to the side as if by centrifugal force. When I looked over the edge of the chasm I could see the other two picking their way carefully down the side, but as they got to the bottom it was obvious why they had never been found. Looking down through the branches and the vegetation on the edge, the outline of a horse at the bottom was totally broken, but even the likelihood of anyone getting that close was remote. It wasn't long before we were all down, and the mares started one by one to walk round in small circles, their noses to the ground, legs slightly bent, picking a suitable spot to lie. Dean and I stayed on our feet and watched over them, dozing, but with our senses nevertheless still alert.

Since it was my name being called, I heard it before Dean, but only just. We both became tense, eyes wide and ears pricked at almost the same instant. The mares, too, lifted their heads and listened.

'No-o-or-man,' and then again, 'No-o-or-man.' What a fool, I thought. Fancy calling me when I had just escaped. It really was a wonder that these humans used us and not the other way round! 'Norma-a-an.' A different voice this time, with the sustained part of the call at the end of the word.

'They must be quite close or we wouldn't hear them at all,' whispered Abergavenny.

'I expect they are at the end of the path,' said Hereford, quietly.

'Or following our tracks up through the wood,' chuckled Stow.

'Ssh!' Dean gave a stern look, but it only made Wold chuckle as well.

'Giggling little idiots, that's all they are,' said Dean in my ear.

The calling was getting fainter now, so in all probability Stow had been right, although I don't suppose Dean would have admitted it.

'I always rather enjoy this, hiding in here while the search goes on all around us.' Abergavenny still spoke in a hushed tone.

'Oh, relax everyone. The excitement is over.' Dean made it sound like an order.

'Hey, Norman, relax.' Abergavenny mimicked Dean's stern attitude.

'What's it like on top of the hill, Abergavenny? Is it very barren and wild?' I asked.

'Call me Abey, most horses do, it's so much easier to say. The hill? No, not really wild, just rather windswept and short of grazing. Covered in a sort of moss, rather than proper grass.'

'I though it might be a bit like being back in Wales, that's all,' I said wistfully.

'No, nothing like that at all. Remember, I come from there as well, so I know what you mean. There are no valleys with little streams in them, nor any heather, and it's really quite a small area; bigger than any field, admittedly, but not the same as having a whole mountain to roam over.' As she spoke, Abey stretched her forelegs out and then walked them back towards her, until she sat like a dog, paused awhile and then got up with a heave and a grunt, finishing the exercise by shaking vigorously. the flies were starting to get bad as the day warmed up, so I moved towards Abey so that we could stand nose to tail and keep them off each other's faces. We must have both dozed off like that, when we were awoken by a loud 'crack!'

'Freeze!' hissed Dean.

It happened again, close to us now. Then it became a regular 'crunch, crunch' of footsteps picking their way through the undergrowth. Nobody moved a muscle. I think I had even stopped breathing. The footsteps had come to a halt.

'Norman?' sharp and enquiring this time. 'Norman?' There was no way of telling whether or not we had been spotted, for it would have been too dangerous to have moved in order to look directly to the top of the quarry. There was nothing to do but remain still.

'Bloody horse!' This was a term I had heard before and knew it not to be one of endearment. 'Crunch, crunch'. The footsteps moved on and declined in volume.

'Phew!' Six horses exhaled together.

'He might have seen us and gone for help.' I was the first to say anything.

'I very much doubt it,' said Dean, reassuringly. 'We must not panic. This is the safest place for us to be today. If we were to move out now, we would be sure to be seen and then they would chase us until you were caught.'

These proved to be words of wisdon, for we heard no more that day, other than the normal noises of the wood. As hunger came on through the day, we spread around the sides and nibbled at the leaves of the few brambles that clung to the edge. Abey and I stayed close to each other and compared notes on the farms that we had originally come from, back in our native land. They seemed to have been very much the same, although Abey had never been in harness, being used only to carry humans at a summer trekking centre. She had been well looked after and much loved by all the holidaymakers to whom she always became very attached. She told of how they would first get on her back, tense and shaking with fright, clutching at the reins and mane together, at the same time digging their heels into her stomach.

'I remember this one little boy,' she said. 'He was put on my back and he screamed and screamed. He screamed so loud that it really hurt my ears. However much I flattened them the noise still got through, and at such a pitch that it seemed to set up a resonance in them. I took a few steps forward, hoping it might give him a bit of confidence, but of course it made matters worse and the screams were joined by him hitting me on my neck with his fists.' She paused in reflection. 'Do you know, by the end of the week he was thumping at my sides with his legs to get me to go faster!'

'What made him change, Abey?' I asked.

'Oh, just patience, I suppose. Bob—who ran the centre with Felicity—plucked him off my back and took him into the house. When they came back the boy had an apple, all cut up into small pieces. Gradually, Felicity got him to give me a few bits, then they had him standing on my back, crawling under my belly and, by the end of the first day, he was letting me walk him around. That evening he must have kept an apple from his supper. He crept out to the paddock, just as the sun was setting to give it to me.'

'Why aren't you still there, Abey? I can see you are not too old for the work and you haven't gone lame or anything like that?' I looked enquiringly at her.

'We all had to go. The horses, ponies, even Bob and Felicity. It was all sold up and the animals all went different ways.' Abey

69

moved to another bunch of briars, leaving me to imagine all those horses and ponies being prodded around Abergavenny Market.

At that time of year the days were very short, so that the few remaining hours before we could all emerge again, soon passed. Dean again took charge of the proceedings by announcing that it was time to go. 'I consider it's safe enough to go out and try to find some grazing.'

'Aren't we going to get away from here?' I was still a bit nervous of staying in the area.

'Later on. There's not a lot to eat up on the hill at the moment so we had better get as much inside us as we can now, then we can move up there before dawn.' He seemed to make sense, as usual. We climbed out into the wood and made our way back to the young plantation where there was enough grass in between the trees for us all to forage. To my right I could see the field that twenty-four hours before had held me captive, whilst over another stone wall in front of me I could see the patch of Christmas trees where I was intended to work. The sledge was no longer lying in the midst of all the trees but had been moved over to the gateway. The spilled trees had all been collected up, as had a great deal more besides, but the presence of the sledge might mean that all hope of using me again had not faded. All of us were hungry, and the night time passed away to the sound of occasional footsteps and the ripping of grass. By dawn, we all had full bellies and were resting on the east slope of the hill, ready to catch the first of the morning sun. Dean led us to this spot which was by a dew pond, where we all had a long drink. I was deep in thought, wondering how water could gather in a pond on top of a hill three hundred metres above sea level, when Abey said: 'I have a good roll and a scrub in here in the summer. It dries out, you know. Just stays damp and muddy.'

'What do you do for water when that happens?' I asked.

'There's a spring over on the northern side, that keeps running most of the time, anyway,' she replied.

'Most of the time? So it can stop?'

'Only once that I can remember.' said Abey casually.

'What do you do then?' I was starting to wonder how they survived.

70

'Graze only when the dew is on the ground—and go thirsty!' She sounded very casual about it.

'How can there be a spring on top of a hill?' I asked, going back to my orginal thought.

'I have never stopped to think about that, but I'm glad there is,' said Abey. Then, turning aside, she added, 'I don't suppose either of you two know, do you?' Stow and Wold looked up with blank expressions.

'Who? What? Us? Know what?'

'Never mind,' said Abey.

'Stow and Wold. What is Stow Fair? Abey said you all got your names from markets, but that doesn't sound like a market.' I thought it was time I got these two into the conversation, and in any case I was curious.

'Oh it is a market, a very big one as it happens, and one of the oldest horse sales in the country.' Stow seemed proud of it.

'People came from miles and miles,' added Wold with a nod, which insinuated that I should have known about it.

'There must be masses and masses of horses there then,' I said.

'Well, it's not just horses, although there are a lot of them.' Wold went on to explain: 'There are lorries, farm machinery, stalls of every kind and description. Market traders are there to sell anything, from tractors to trinkets or trench coats to "T" shirts!'

'There used to be five hundred horses through the sale ring, but there were only half that amount on the day we were there,' added Stow.

'Apart from the travellers' horses, that is,' said Wold.

'What horses are those, then?' I asked.

'It's really a travellers or gypsy, fair. They have been granted a Charter, to allow them to set up stalls in the Square and also to park their caravans on the side of the road for the duration of the Fair. Then, quite apart from the official auction, they trade amongst themselves. dealing in ponies and horses; they even parade their stallions up and down the road. I am told that these travellers come to the Fair from all over the country. A sort of get-together more than anything else. A tradition for them now.' Wold seemed well informed on the subject.

'Did you have to come far to it?' I addressed this to both of them.

'Not very far, no.' Stow was the first to answer. 'We were always on the move, you ...' Wold was stopped by a black look from Stow.

'We lived in lots of places.' Stow was trying hard to cover for Wold.

'Always together in your travels, though?' I enquired.

'We even pulled the s-s-same... ' Wold hesitated as Stow glowered.

'Same caravan?' I finished the sentence for her. They both nodded in confirmation.

'Why are you trying to keep it from me? I mean, why do you seem to be ashamed about it?' My question left them puzzled. 'I would like to bet that you enjoyed yourselves. Plenty going on all the time, a responsible job to do pulling somebody's home around behind you. Meeting different horses and going all over the country. It doesn't sound bad to me. Given the chance you would probably both go back to it again.'

'Like so many things, it was all right in the spring and summer but, come winter, it could be hell if we hadn't got a good pitch with a bit of grass and shelter nearby.' Stow was more relaxed already.

'I liked the life.' Wold obviously felt more free to talk now. 'We were part of the family, our masters depended on us and treated us well.'

'Land Rover!' Hereford leapt to her feet as she shouted.

'Where?' I tried to see which way she was looking.

'Land Rover there, down by the gate.' I followed her eyes and sure enough, there was Glyn's Land Rover lurching its way over the ruts towards a rusty metal gate.

'Norman, go and hide down by the wood,' said Dean. 'We'll stay here as if you weren't with us.'

'I'm going with him, Dean,' said Abey. 'In case he gets lost.'

'Abey, don't ... ' Whatever Dean had said was lost to the wind as we set off towards the trees and out of sight. Unfortunately, the eastern side of the hill was better fenced than the western side where we had been for the last two days, so that it was not possible for horses to get through. The sheep had their 'windows' on this side, but that was no good to us. To try and reach the western side now would have been futile, for to do so would have meant crossing a large tract of open ground where we would certainly be spotted. Abey knew the terrain well, and shouted for me to follow her. She was heading down off the skyline, making for the dark edge of the wood. From the very moment we set off, the best hiding place must have been at the back of her mind. We headed straight for it. Down to the side of the wood and then alongside it, until we came to a slight valley running at right angles to the fence. As we turned up it, the bottom felt wet and soft. Abey slowed to a walk then halted, where the edges were at their highest.

'This is the best we can do on this part of the hill.' She puffed at the exertion.

'You remembered this place quickly!' I complimented her.

'This is the stream from the spring I was telling you about, earlier. The one we have to use in summer.' We stood close together, listening for the sound of an engine. It wasn't long before we heard it chugging over the open ground. Glyn must have been searching the whole area, for the strangled exhaust note came and went several times. When it did eventually stop very close to us, I knew that Glyn had guessed where I might be. Whilst I watched the edge of the valley waiting for him, I could feel that Abey's eyes were on me, wondering what I might do. She must have guessed that in all probability I would go with him, for she suddenly swung away and shouted at me to follow her again. She trotted noisily up the stream bed until it had risen to ground level and we could see Glyn's vehicle parked by the wood, not far from where we had been. He was standing by it, talking with Matt, and must have seen us at about the same time as we spotted them. Abey, too, had seen them, and as they moved to get back into the Land Rover, we quickened our pace, out into the open, over the skyline once more and back down the western side of the hill. We had got back into the wood long before there was any sign of the two men, and I do not know whether they ever bothered to

74

give chase or not. I knew the way now and took over the lead. Straight back to the clearing at the end of the path, from there through the trees, and then back down into the hiding place. Neither of us spoke for a long time, each probably realising that sooner or later I would have to return to my routine world, where horses still had to work.

'I can't go on living in this quarry by day and grazing in the trees by night. That's less freedom that I had before.' Abey didn't reply, so I went on, 'Later on, after it has got dark, I will make my way back to the field. At least if I turn up there I might avoid having to pull any more of those Christmas trees!'

'I'll come with you,' announced Abey.

'It's a long way and you probably won't get back by dawn.' Despite this, I hoped she would come with me.

'That doesn't matter. If anybody finds me all they'll do is lead me back onto the hill and let me go again. So, whatever happens, I will always get back to my home.' She had a delightful way of seeing through to the simplest solution to any problem. Later that evening we followed the usual routine—climbed out of the quarry, left the cover of the trees, grazed in the same place as the last two nights but then, instead of turning up towards the top of the hill, we scrambled over the wall into the wretched Christmas trees. As we came level with the spot where I had turned the sledge over, I told Abey what I had done there three days previously.

'You may be going back, but I'm not so sure they will welcome you' she said between fits of laughter.

As we came to the gate onto the track, we both stopped and looked wisfully towards the distant outline of the sugar loaf with the black mountains to its right, and the Brecon Beacons just showing beyond. There wasn't anything to say, though, as we both knew the thought in each other's mind. Following the track back was easy, as we wandered side by side through the night. It was only when we were at the turning before the gate to my field, that I suddenly felt that it would be very lonely back in there, after the good company I had had over the last three days.

'I wonder if the gate is open?' Abey's practical mind at work again.

'Not only open, but the field is probably full of Martha and her gang.'

Open, yes but the field was completely empty. It had never looked so deserted and unfriendly. After standing in the gateway for a while, I said: 'Come in and have a look at my one and a half acres.' Abey came in through the gate and stayed until after dawn.

'I had better go now. I wouldn't want your boss to come and shut the gate with me in here as well.' I didn't really agree, but nodded just the same. Abey didn't leave, though, because as soon as she went out through the gate she turned right, back into the wood instead of the way we had come, and then up to where I was, but on the outside of the hedge. There she stayed, until Glyn drove by.

As always, I heard the Land Rover a long way off. It was going much faster than normal and didn't slow up when it came to my gateway. Indeed, it didn't slow up at all, but continued across the bottom of the field at an unabated pace.

I had just begun to feel hurt that, after all my good intentions in returning, I was now not even going to be noticed when the old vehicle let out a terrible shriek. It shuddered in its efforts to come to a halt, and one wheel let out a grating sound as it out-performed its fellows and ceased to turn. When it did come to a standstill slightly out of line with the road, lumps of mud fell from its underside, dislodged by the violent vibration. Next came the sound of metal under extreme stress, as reverse gear was selected, and Glyn steered an erratic course back to the gate, which he promptly shut. I turned to Abey, poised to speak, only to find that she had gone. I could just hear the sound of breaking branches as she moved swiftly through the wood. Glyn came up the field, obviously pleased to see me, although more than a little surprised. A large helping of oats was his expression of gratitude, as well as a lot of fuss and patting.

The bowl wasn't even empty before Glyn returned, with Matt this time. The tack was produced from the back of the vehicle and we were off, Matt on my back. It was a long trek. All the way between the woods, past Kit's field and then by Moat Wood and Cid's field. I looked up towards the higher ground as I went past the gate where I had first seen Kit, but there was no sign of any horses there. I wondered if the fox had got over there that night and whether he had found a mate or not.

Horror of horrors! There ahead, by the entrance to the farm, stood my sledge. The spring went out of my step that instant. I felt betrayed, as if I had been led to believe that something better had been in store for that day. In my disappointment I had failed to notice that in addition to the sledge, there were several vehicles, other than Glyn's and many people standing around, but only a small heap of trees already tied and even loaded onto one of the farm trailers. As soon as we reached the group of people Matt jumped down, and a girl I had never seen before started to brush my mane. This certainly was different. Mane first, then the tail and finally all the mud was brushed off my coat, even the long strands of hair around my feet were spruced up.

Whilst all this was happening there seemd to be a lot of planning going on. Cameras were set up on tripods, my sledge had been placed by the trailer and was being carefully loaded by Matt. Another girl was wiping a damp cloth over the harness, which had been temporarily removed. By the time I was led to where Matt had been loading, I felt as I had never felt before. My mane and tail bounced as I moved, and my coat lay flat and sleek to my sides, showing the working of each rippling muscle. I was harnessed up, moved to a predetermined position, someone shouted and, with Matt by my side, set off to the accompaniment of a whirr or camera. This process was repeated three times, and then I was left to stand still while the trees were unloaded by Matt and Glyn, also for the benefit of the cameras.

I went back to my field a proud horse. The glow of pride was still with me when I heard the sound of a horse getting close to my field. In all the excitement I had completely forgotten Abey!

'I thought you had gone back,' I said in surprise.

'Never mind me. What on earth has happened to you since I last saw you?' She was even more surprised than I had been. I told her all about the day—about the grooming and the filming. Of course she knew all about grooming, and admitted it was one of the things she missed most.

'Well! I'm honoured to know you, Sir!' she said mockingly, when I had finished.

'What about you? How is it you are still here, and not on the hill?'

'I haven't seen anyone all day,' she replied. 'Found a nice spot in the wood and lay up there for the day. I'll go back the way we came later on tonight.'

'Since nobody really cares where you are, you can come out and see me now and then. We can have a chat, compare our lives and keep in touch.' I felt everything was working out well for me.

'I think that's a good idea, Norman. We'll keep in touch' she agreed.

I never did have to go back to work on the other side of the hill. Whether those to whom I had been loaned thought that I was no use, or that they themselves were incapable of handling me, I don't know but, either way, I was not sorry to see the last of Christmas trees for that year. In fact, I now had quite a long break without any work at all.

6
A CHOKING EXPERIENCE

One of my regular visitors during this time was my friend the fox from the other end of the wood, the one who came through Kit's field every night. Although I had never seen him here before, it was not long after my voluntary return that he appeared.

'Hallo, Norman.' For once I had seen him coming. 'I hear you've been up to all sorts of tricks!'

'How could you know about that?' I answered.

'How could I not? The whole wood, the whole area is talking about it!' The fox went on, 'We have a very good bush telegraph here, you see. You probably didn't see them, but there are some ravens living on top of Oldhill, and they keep an eye on everything that goes on up there. They saw five horses grazing one day, then suddenly, three days later there were six.'

'That doesn't mean anything, surely.' I felt I had been spied upon.

'Not in itself, no, but then they saw Glyn's Land Rover and you and that grey running off together into the wood on the other side of the hill. They happened to tell some crows about it and one of them told it to one of the jays. From then on there was no stopping the story.'

'How embarrassing,' I said, picturing all those animals appearing one by one to tell me that they had heard what I had been up to, and 'weren't you naughty' they would all say with a reproachful shake of the head.

'What about you, Mr. Fox?'

'Call me Charlie,' he interrupted.

'OK, Charlie, what have you been up to? Did you see Cid the night that I provided you with all those mice to eat?'

'Eventually, but I didn't bless you for having to find him,' he replied.

'You didn't have to see him,' I said.

'Maybe not, but I felt that it was a sort of errand. Anyway, he wasn't in the field when I got there so I asked around a bit. One of the owls told me he was in a stable at night, and showed me how to get there.'

'What was so difficult about that?'

'The stable yard, that's what. I crept up to where the owl had told me to go but I couldn't see any horse there. I stood up on my hind legs to try and see over the door, but it was far too high for that. I was just trying to see under the door when something moved in the stable alongside. I moved over and whispered, 'Cid, is that you?' He got to his feet, which was a noisy affair, and looked over the door. When he saw me he pulled back, and before I could stop him he let out the most terrible snort.'

'I don't suppose he was expecting to see a fox looking up at him.'

'I wasn't that keen on the horse looking at me, either, and I certainly didn't know there was a dog there as well.' He looked me accusingly in the eye.

'A dog? There wasn't a dog there when I stayed in that stable,' I said in self-defence.

'Well, there sure is now. Fortunately he is shut away, but I didn't know that at first. As soon as Cid had snorted, this dog must have woken up, for he started to bark and bark. I don't know if the idiot knew what he was barking at, but bark he did. Even if I had tried to speak to Cid it would have been difficult to make myself heard.'

'Are you telling me that, after all this, you never even spoke to Cid?'

'That's right. Look, there is only one way out of that yard. If you have been there, you know. It only needed that dog to wake someone up and that would be the end. Dogs frighten me, anyway.' He seemed slightly embarrassed to admit it.

'Why dogs? I should have thought that you could have outwitted them any day.' It didn't seem like him to be so easily frightened.

'You will see one day.' He left it at that and clearly didn't want to discuss the matter any further.

'Thanks for trying, anyway.' I closed the subject. 'But what about the rest of the night? How did that go?'

'Very well, thanks. I was away for three nights in all. Got as far as Farm Wood. I've got a lot of friends over there. Easy digging and a rubish tip nearby—a good spot for the lazy.' He paused and then changed the subject. 'Have you been down into the lower part of this wood recently?' I told him that, apart from the session with the Christmas trees, I hadn't actually been in there at all.

'Well, there is an enormous clearing being made right in the middle of the trees. A lot of the animals think there is going to be a lake there. Thought you might know more about it, that's all.'

I apologised for my ignorance on the subject. He then went on to tell me the latest in Oldhill Wood gossip, ending up with a vivid description of how one of the ewes that had been in my field had died after getting inextricably caught up in some brambles. Not content with that, he went on to tell how he, with at least two other foxes, stoats, crows, rats, voles and a badger, had all argued over the clearing up of the remains. I suspected that it was this last piece of information that he had really come to tell me, for he left with a sly grin on his face, leaving me to contemplate the fate of an acquaintance. I was only glad that he wasn't able to tell me which one it was.

Farm Wood, where Charlie had so many friends, was where Matt and I were to part company. We went there to work amongst some chestnut trees that had just been felled at fifteen years of age. After this they would be allowed to coppice, producing lots of shoots from the same stump, and cleared again every twenty-five years. The first cut is always the easiest to work amongst, for the poles are straighter than those cut after coppicing.

Whilst working in this wood I was to be put into a field by the farm buildings, in the company of Rannoch. He was a fine-looking horse, belonging to the daughter of the farm manager. His coat was a deep brown, with black mane and tail, and his legs went from brown to black as they got towards his fetlocks, so that all four feet were jet black. The muzzle was tapered towards his flared nostrils, with a star between his eyes. He was to prove to be both interesting and knowledgeable company.

The first day's work in Farm Wood was exhausting. The journey over from my field had been easy and uneventful, but as soon as the tack had been fitted, I realised that something was badly amiss. My usual collar had never really recovered from the pounding it had had to withstand when we were in the Larch trees. It had got to the stage where it looked more suited to a scarecrow than a working horse. It had split in several places around the rim, from which the straw stuffing was slowly oozing. Many other parts had been reinforced with string to prevent it completely falling apart. Now another one had been found. New it was not, but it did look more intact than its predecessor. When first fitted it seemed to sit perched high up on my neck, not resting on my shoulders as my regular one had. When it came under the stress of work, though, it was to cause me the most enormous problem. Instead of being pulled into the shoulder by the weight of the timber behind it, the collar remained on my neck. It was pulled to the angle of the shoulder, as it is designed to be, but being on my neck it merely had the effect of strangulation. The harder the work, the less I could breathe.

For the first few days the work was not heavy nor did there seem to be a rush to move a great quantity of timber, so that between each tush it was possible to pause and let my lungs take in as much air as possible before returning to hitch up to the next suffocating load.

That first evening I complained bitterly to Rannoch about my collar. He had every sympathy with me, and we thought a lot about ways to try and prevent it happening again the next day, but without any success. I finally fell asleep hoping that Rannoch's theory, that the collar had been out of use for so long and thus had become unduly stiff and unyielding, might prove to be correct.

Matt appeared with the same collar the next morning but it didn't feel any different when it was fitted. We left the farm and climbed the hill behind to get up to the wood. The whole way up I tossed my head from side to side and up and down, in the vain hope that he might look further to see what was causing the discomfort, but it didn't seem to arouse any curiosity at all. The whole day was a repeat performance.

'You will have to go till you drop,' said Rannoch that evening. 'Then they'll think there is something wrong with your lungs. I don't suppose anyone will ever look at anything so obvious as your collar.'

I was beginning to become resigned to a similar viewpoint myself. During the day I had been practising lowering my neck, so that nearly all the weight of the timber came in a straighter pull. This way I felt that it would be possible to carry on working, provided the weight of the timber did not increase nor the pace at which we were working.

My thoughts on the subject were interrupted that evening by two magpies, who had arrived simultaneously at the same hawthorn bush which both of them intended to occupy for the night. Their whole performance was carried out in complete silence, as each one knew exactly what the other meant by his or her actions. To start with, they sat on opposite sides of the bush, each pretending to be unaware of the other's presence. They hopped around a bit, testing the branches and the suitability of the site. If one particular branch appeared to have possibilities, then a certain amount of organising of the branches around it would take place. A twig would be siezed in the beak then pushed this way and that, and then finally left precisely where it was in the first place. The female bird was considerably more active in the branch arranging than the male, who although he did a bit of it now and then, spent much more time staring out of the tree. It seemed to me that the female did know where she wanted to be, for there was one particular spot to which she would return over and over again. Each time she went there she would have a good shake, puff up her feathers then sink down until the soft feathers that covered her underside absorbed her feet into their warm embrace. What disturbed her instantly was the male landing on the same branch as soon as she had gone through this routine. At that stage she would become quite aggressive and chase him to the outer branches, not returning to her chosen spot until she had gone through the whole process of selection once more. If, as occasionally happened, the male moved towards the chosen branch, he was instantly set upon and again ousted to the further regions of the bush. This performance was repeated over and over, from the moment the sun weakened behind Farm Wood until well after dark. Then he was allowed to get closer, but then only by degrees; too bold a move would lead to a peck, whilst each advance was met by a display of discomfort, shown by a restless shuffle of the feet, or a re-adjustment to the feathers. Finally, he managed to get onto the same branch without any physical aggression and stayed there until dawn. What was all the more amazing about this magpie performance was that it went on night after night. When I first watched it, I assumed incorrectly that I was witnessing a rare event.

Nothing improved at work over the next few days, but then it didn't get any worse either. Every morning Rannoch and I would try and devise some way of letting Matt know what was wrong. All that happened was that he got more and more impatient with my behaviour, as I either refused to let him fit the collar or made out that the relatively small logs were too heavy to pull.

One evening I returned to the field to find it empty. No sign of Rannoch at all. It was not long before I heard a horse walking over the concrete in the farmyard and guessed it would be him coming back. I had been strangely disappointed when, on returning from work, there had been no horse present to whom I could complain about my trials and tribulations. Being able to have a good moan at the end of the day had made everything about the problem more bearable. In a strange way, I think I almost looked forward to it. It was all the more disappointing, therefore, when Rannoch came into view being ridden. Horse and rider both came into the field, whereupon they immediately went to the corner nearest the farm buildings. Although I had not noticed it before, in this corner – the most level part of the field – there was an oval-shaped track trodden out of the grass. Very symmetrical, with each side parallel. To my amazement Rannoch and rider commenced to go round and round, firstly just walking but then at a slow trot, changing direction and doing the same thing the other way about. I moved over to have a closer look.

'Are you all right?' I whispered, as he came by me. He didn't even turn his head but, as he passed next time, he did manage to say out of the side of his mouth, 'Just stay there and watch.'

'Can't you go for a proper ride?' I asked a few laps further on.

'Later. I'll tell you later.' He seemed very short of breath, as if what he was doing was very energetic. I moved away a few paces, meaning to leave him alone until he was let loose later, but turned again out of curiosity to watch a bit more and found myself compelled to keep watching for the next half hour. His movements appeared graceful and effortless, although I knew from his speech that the latter was not so. Several movements followed one another, like a dance routine. One moment he would be walking from one corner in a relaxed way with his head low, only to change to a brisk and alert walk followed almost instantly by trotting. This trot was either active and precise, or at other times, usually going from corner to corner, it would become a much longer stride so that he threw his forelegs out in front of him, where they seemed to hang in the air a momentarily prior to being flicked back to earth. The cantering was all done at a slow pace, whilst in all paces 'S' shapes and circles both large and small, were being described on the ground. It was a fascinating display that added a lot of stature to an already good-looking horse. He had given the sort of show that I imagined the thoroughbred racing stallions might well give before their prospective brides.

'Rannoch, that was very impressive,' I told him when he eventually got back to the field, having been off for the 'proper' ride I had mentioned earlier.

'Thank you, Norman.' He looked genuinely pleased that I had been complimentary.

'Why do . . . umm . . . I mean, what . . .'

'I know what you are trying to ask,' Rannoch ended my search for the right words, 'but I'm not sure I know the answer myself. It is very important to Mother because we do a lot of it.'

'Who is Mother?' I asked.

'Mother? Oh, yes, Mother!' He had a short chuckle to himself. 'That is Jill, my owner. All event horses talk about their owners as 'mother'.

'Can't see myself calling Matt "father",' I said quietly.

'Oh you wouldn't.' He had heard my aside. 'Only female owners; the others are just "the boss".' That is even more inappropriate, I thought.

'You must enjoy it a bit or you couldn't make it look so good.' I returned to the original subject.

'Most days I do, as long as we don't do too much of it. You have to be in the mood or have someone watching, like you today.' He went on to tell me how it was only one part of a more complicated competition, and how the two of them travelled miles to go to such events, sometimes staying overnight. Of the other two phases to be done, one was Show Jumping, which clearly bored him for he dismissed it very rapidly. 'Last but not least is the Cross-Country.' There was a sparkle in his eye at the mere mention of it.

'Is that a race?' My question was met by a stern look from Rannoch.

'Good heavens, no!' The thought of it appalled him. He paused in reflection, and then added, 'Though to see some of them go you would think it was. But no, it's not a race, and to treat it as such would surley end in disaster.'

'What is it, then?' I pushed him to explain.

'Oh sorry, I was just picturing some of the accidents from last season.' He took a deep breath and continued. 'What we have to do is follow a course that has been set out for us, but it won't be over just grass fields. It will include jumps over . . .'

'You jump hedges and ditches, like Cid!' I interrupted.

'No, no, that's hunting,' he corrected me. 'We do jump hedges and ditches, but they are one hell of a lot bigger than anything Cid

86

is going to come across out hunting. Not only that, but we have to go over really big jumps—as high as a pony—and made out of big logs. Then, to make it even more difficult, some of those jumps are placed close to one another so that we have to land in such a way that we can take off again for the next one. Sometimes we even have to jump into or out of water, and that is really difficult, because the water slows up your feet as they hit it but the body keeps going at the same pace as before. Lots end up in the water, especially the riders.'

'Don't a lot of you get badly hurt doing it?' I asked him.

'I wouldn't say badly hurt, but a lot do go lame and then have to have a long rest before they can start again.' He seemed to be excluding himself from these problems.

'Surely you must get hurt sometimes?' I thought that he might have assumed he was safe from such problems.

'Oh yes, both of us do, but as far as I know we haven't missed an event because of injury yet. Mind you, both of us came down at the end of last season. It was a good job it was at the end, for we were both very sore after that.'

'What caused that? Water?' I tried not to sound too anxious to hear the details of the accident.

'No, it should have been a simple jump really, but a lot of horses came to grief there.' Rannoch left it at that, so I prompted him with:

'Why? If it was so easy?'

'The jump was simple enough, but to get to it in the right way wasn't easy.' I got the sort of look from him that tells you how difficult it is to explain something to someone who has no idea what you are talking about. Now that he had started to explain, though, he was going to see it through.

'As I said, the jump was simple. Just a pallisade with a log in front of it as a ground line.' He paused to see if I was following the description but instantly saw from my expression that I was once more lost.

'Right.' He faked his impatience, as I could see that he was really quite enjoying himself. 'A pallisade is a horizontal pole which has between itself and the ground a series of vertical pieces of timber, giving the overall effect of a sturdy section of garden fence.' I nodded in confirmation that I understood so far. 'A ground line is where a pole, ditch or anything for that matter, is placed on the ground in front of a jump to stop horses getting too close to the bottom, thereby being unable to clear the uppermost part.'

'It makes you spread out a bit, then, instead of just going up and down.' I thought I understood.

'Exactly. Now I can go on.' He was pleased with his pupil. 'The jump was approached from almost alongside it, through a very slow combination of small jumps, necessitating a sweeping 'U' turn to line up for it correctly. Add to that the fact that it was also on a downhill slope, and you have all the ingredients for a problem fence.'

'How did you and Mother go wrong, then?', I asked.

'Like most horses, I started to turn as soon as I saw where the next jump was. Mother tried to stop me, which put us off balance. Then, because it was downhill we were going far too slowly.' By now he was re-living the whole episode.

'I still don't see why you both fell.'

'The worst is yet to come. As we got close to the jump I could see that my stride was going to put my forefeet right into the log that was the ground line. By then, though, it was too late to shorten and take off a bit sooner, because we were going so slowly that any loss of momentum would have meant that we couldn't possibly have cleared the whole jump. I tried to stop. My feet slid on the grass so that for one last stride I put my forefeet in between the pole and the pallisade itself, the last bit of forward motion being absorbed by the upright part of the fence.' I drew breath to speak but he hadn't finished. 'Oh no, it didn't end there, I'm afraid. Many horses had done precisely the same thing before me, so that the fence had by now become extremely weak. As my full weight came against it, it gave. Not a lot, but with my head, neck and part of my shoulders already over, there was nothing I could do when Mother also landed heavily around my ears. The pair of us cartwheeled over the top, to land in a heap on the other side. Very lucky to get away with nothing more than a lot of burises.'

'It all sounds very dangerous to me. I think you are very brave to go and do it all again.' The compliment made him draw up to his full height. Then he turned and said:

'I heard something about you the other day that sounded even worse.' It was well into the night by the time I had finished telling him about the escapade with the runaway log.

Whether it was thought I was ill, or simply that I was not needed that day I don't know, but much to my relief nobody came to collect me so that I had the pleasure of watching all the activity around the farm. In the early afternoon Rannoch and I heard the approach of a horse, and who should appear but Cid. He was as surprised to see me as I him. In fact he stopped dead in his tracks, for which he was reprimanded with a sharp smack of the whip.

'Hi, Cid!' I shouted across the fence. 'What are you doing here?'

'Moving lambs, I think.' He only just managed to reply, before going into the yard. He came back out again a few minutes later, in the company of four people I had never seen before, although I did recognise Mark riding him. They all carried long lengths of black plastic pipe and looked set for a battle.

'Lambs it is!' he said as he went by. 'See you later.'

'Oyee ... Hup! ...!' The noise and its variety defies description. If the devil himself were trying to round up his star followers I doubt there would be more noise! Presently they came into view. A sea of white, speckled with bobbing black dots. In front a man, in danger of being overwhelmed by the tide behind him, whilst to the rear was Cid, three men and a dog. Cid appeared to be responsible for cutting off the line of retreat should any of the lambs decide they would rather return from whence they came, and many did make a brave effort to do just that. The dog was responsible for both sides, a task that appeared to be taxing his ability to be in two places at once while still maintaining his sanity. The whole group appeared to be in a frenzy. As they drew level with the field so a handful of enterprising lambs made a determined escape bid. Seeing the inviting grass on our side of the fence, they squeezed their tiny frames between the lower rails and shot away up the field.

The dog saw the move at once and cast an eye back to his master for confirmation. A wave of the hand was enough for he came at the fence at full stretch, clearing the top rail cleanly. The lambs, having initially got away from the flock, now felt vulnerable on their own and called out for mum. The sight of the dog brought on a feeling of panic as they careered wildly down the field, only to crash into the fence at the bottom, this time quite unable to get through as smoothly as they had before.

Whilst some of them made it to the other side, others turned and ran up the field again, pursued by the dog. It was a long while before they were all reunited with the main flock. During all this Cid was prancing about at the rear, ensuring that not one of the little blighters passed him by. Mark, sitting astride him, didn't appear to have to control him at all and the horse was putting on quite a show in front of Rannoch and I.

Once all were 'safely gathered in', Cid was brought out and tied to the gate near us.

'Phew!' he exclaimed. 'That is the hardest work I ever have to do.'

'You seemed to be enjoying it!' I replied.

'Oh yes, it's great. Could do without the boss on top, though,' he said.

'You wouldn't know where to go,' I told him.

'Of course I would! And I could do it all a lot faster. Damn nearly fall over sometimes with all that weight stuck up above.' Cid seemed certain about his ability to work on his own, and I must confess I think he probably could have done it very well.

I told him about the fox coming over to see him with a message, and then about my three days' exile on Oldhill, both of which he had already heard about such is the efficiency of the bush telegraph.

'What was the hunting like?' I asked, when I had finished telling him all my news.

'Marvellous!' he said. 'We went to some new areas this season. Much smarter packs, and don't they go!' He cast his eyes towards the sky as he spoke.

'Surprised you could keep up,' I said, pulling his leg.

'Keep up! Do you know, one day we must have gone for eight or nine . . .' Mark reached forward to untie the reins and lead him away. 'Tell you next time I see you,' he said over his shoulder as Mark got on.

It was two days before the misery started anew. Matt came in the morning and fitted the same tight collar around my neck. I continued the struggle as before, managing to keep working at the same slow pace and taking a breather between each tush. All the time I had a feeling that matters could only get worse. The inevitable happened when it got to the end of the week and Matt had to make up his wages. Suddenly, instead of having one log at a time behind me, the tushes were doubled up. Struggling as I did it was still impossible to take two logs the whole distance from the stump to the stack, however much Matt encouraged me to do so. Poor Matt, I'm sure that at the time he had no idea what he was putting me through. His only concern was taking home a wage at the end of the week that his family could live off. Instead of following behind me as I pulled the logs, he now came to my head to encourage me to keep going. I could see that he was also working extremely hard, on the move the whole time, either behind hitching up or pulling me along from in front. At the slightest excuse I would stop for a breather, then Matt, seeing that the tush had caught a stump or was tangled in a branch, would rush back and free it so that we could continue.

On each successive trip it felt as if the collar was getting tighter. The sun had come out and sapped the last bit of oxygen from the air. It looked as if it should have been a hot day, and indeed I was wet all over from the sweat pouring off me yet I did not feel hot, not even warm. In fact I was very cold, the slightest breeze that there was sending shivers through my damp body.

A lump had formed in my throat, hard and dry, and lodged itself firmly at the base preventing the passage of what little air I could get. The pain in the area surrounding this lump became intense. My field of vision was also narrowing. No longer did I manage to see through a full 270 degrees, only one subject at a time coming into focus. Matt's hand came to the bridle but, as it got close, I only saw the side of his face as he drew alongside. I felt a tug, heard no word or encouragement, but moved forward. The pull now came at an angle. I moved to the side to lessen it, tripped and came down on my knees. I felt Matt pulling again and thought I heard him saying something. I tried to look and see what he wanted but all I could make out was the line of the River Severn far below us. I could spot the bend just after Newnham, where the water clung to the western bank leaving a large mud flat on the opposite side, then the gradual widening on the next bend as it came back onto course and passed Hock Cliff. Then, just after Frampton it grew into a lake, before it came to the Wildfowl Trust at Slimbridge. Matt's face blotted out the view after that. His face appeared as a caricature of its normal self; immensely long and narrow, with highly pronounced cheek bones below which the cheeks themselves looked to be sucked in. His nose was hooked like that of a bird of prey and the chin jutted so far out towards me that the end of it was out of focus. The eyes were deep and recessed into dark pits, and as I watched his mouth opened to reveal the occasional tooth, yellow with age, brown where they happened to adjoin one another. As the mouth moved so I felt the warm breath in my nostrils. The smell was pungent, a mixture of onion and nicotine. I was still vaguely aware of verbal and physical encouragement, but I could no longer tell in which direction I was supposed to be moving. The thought of lying down for a few minutes appealed to me. I started to look to one side so that I could pick a spot free of logs and branches but, as I swung my head around, my whole body followed it. The ground was warm and soft. How clever I had been to find such a glorious place to rest . . .

7
A SIGHT OF THE HUNT

There was a strong smell of baked mud—Glyn's Land Rover. He must have come to feed me early today. I pulled my legs up under my body so as to rise, then paused. It had been a great effort just to do that. In any case, I could now see that it wasn't even my field. Then it all came flooding back. The collar, Matt's face, the pain and, finally, the peace of lying down and ignoring the whole lot. I didn't know what Glyn was doing, although he was fussing around me. The collar and most of the tack had gone, but I could feel that I was still lying on some of it. Other than that it was cold, bitterly cold. How long I had been lying in this position I did not know, but my coat was still very wet. Glyn was at my head encouraging me to get up. I lay prone. There didn't seem to be any point in doing anything different. At least the part of my body that was in contact with the ground was not cold. If anything, it would be nice to just roll over and warm up the exposed side.

93

Even if I did get up it would be impossible for me to make it to the bottom of the hill. All in all I might just as well stay put. Shutting my eyes again I realized that I had not seen Matt. I wondered what had become of him.

My next awakening was to the sound of strange voices. Glyn was still there, but there were now two others with him. One was standing between us and the edge of the wood and was shouting to the other, and all three appeared to be nodding in agreement. Glyn was at my head again, urging me to rise. The other man was less subtle but more persuasive. He stood at my back and prodded me with a stick and didn't cease until it was clear that I was indeed making a good effort to regain my feet. At my third attempt I was up, very unsteady, with the feeling gone from all four legs where they had been tucked under my body. As I swayed this way and that, Glyn moved to my side as if to add extra support. Knowing that he could not possibly stop me if I fell and that I would undoubtedly squash him if he tried, had a electrifying effect on me and I soon managed to stand erect. Whilst waiting for my balance to improve I noticed that the other man had moved right to the boundary of the wood and now stood by the small gate, which he opened as he beckoned us over. I shifted my weight from one leg to the other as an indication that all was well, and that in my opinion I was fit to move again. Towards the gate we went, very slowly, and with great deliberation. Once through, the last vestiges of tack were removed and all three men went back to the gate and left me alone. Without moving my body I surveyed as much as possible, but since I appeared to be on the very side of the hill, there was not much in the immediate vicinity to be seen. Apart from the wood behind, the ground fell away in every direction. In any case, I really didn't care where I was. I turned round on the spot to see Glyn and his friends looking over the gate at me. I wished they would go away. Thinking it might help to get rid of them if I looked more normal, I sampled some of the grass, and although it felt fresh when cropped off, by the time it had passed my muzzle it was dry and coarse. It stuck to the roof of my mouth and between my teeth and it was difficult to spit it all out. Still feeling cold I sought shelter from the edge of the wood, where I found a slight dip in the ground over which the unruly hedgerow trees hung. here I lay down again. Before Glyn finally left, he came back to check on me. He pulled my ears and gave me a mint.

I must have got up and turned around at some time during the night, for I was facing the opposite way when I next fully awoke. It was the loud-mouthed foxes that woke me. What a terrible noise they can come out with in the dead of night!

'Thought you were a gonna, mate,' said the red muzzle peering at me.

'That makes two of us,' I replied with conviction.

'What's up then? Old age? Guts ache? Overworked?'

'Just a bit choked with life,' I said, feeling quite chirpy after my long sleep.

'Choked, eh? I wish I had something to choke on. Too many damn foxes in this wood. Can't find a thing to eat anywhere.'

'Ah, yes,' I said, remembering my friend's visit to this wood. 'Charlie said it was a bit crowded over here.'

'Charlie? Charlie who? Whole place is full of Charlies.'

'Just a fox I know over in Oldhill Wood,' I said.

'Oh. That Charlie. 'E didn't stop 'ere long. Likes 'is independence, I reckon.'

'Seemed to think you had it easy over here,' I told him, 'said something about a rubbish tip and plenty to eat.'

'Don't go there no more. Too bloody dangerous,' then, without pausing, he let out another of those terrible yowls. 'Ark! Hey, Vix, come o'er. That 'orse be still 'ere.' Vix came up to him and sat down. 'What's your name, mate?' he turned to look at me.

'Norman,' I said, 'and yours?'

'Well, Norman, this is Vix and I'm Rey.'

'Hi, Vix, Rey.'

'Say 'ello' said Rey to Vix, who was busy trimming her toes with her teeth.

'Hi,' she said, without even looking up.

'We don't go to the tip no more, do we, Vix?'

'Nah,' she said, still without looking up.

'Not since a couple of us got trapped there, we 'aven't,' he went on.

'Got their heads stuck in a tin, did they?' I asked him.

'Oh no, not that sort of trapped. Trapped by 'umans is wot I mean. Bloody snares, tight round a neck or a leg.'

'Why do they want to do that to you?' It sounded as if Charlie had had a lucky escape.

'Don't rightly know. Done nothing wot would 'arm 'em, 'ave we, Vix?' said Rey, turning to his friend. 'We 'aven't, 'ave we?' he said again, having got no response the first time.

'Nah,' came the predictable reply.

'Talkative friend you've got there, Rey' I said, hoping to raise some response.

'Don't like to be reminded of it, see,' she said. 'I was one wot found one of 'em see.'

'I see,' I said flippantly.

'Weren't a pretty sight.' Rey had taken over the conversation again. 'Cousin of 'ers damn near chewed 'is leg off trying to get free.' The thought made my hair stand on end, but I didn't say anything.

'That ain't the end of it, neither,' he went on. 'Whilst Vix was there, young lad came up, smelt o' death she reckons, and beat cousin to death wi' a stick.'

I was so horrified by this tale that I leapt to my feet, poised for some sort of action, though there was nothing to be done. Suddenly the discomfort had become too much for me to take lying down, but matters didn't improve on my feet, although the hair on my back could be shaken down into position once more.

'Not nice, eh?' said Rey, seeing my state of shock.

'Isn't there something you can do to stop it?' I asked, knowing full well that there wasn't.

'Twas only a few days later that t'other one got 'ad. Round neck 'e was.'

'Did Vix find him as well?' I asked.

'No, was old Charlie as we call 'im, wot found this 'un. Been 'ere long time 'e 'as, knows it all like. Even 'e couldn't get 'im loose. Tried, mind. Swears 'e'd loosened noose,' Rey said admiringly.

'Why couldn't the fox get out if he had loosened the snare?' I asked.

''Cos 'e ran owt o' time, din'e. Lad came to check on snare.'

'I suppose he beat him to death, like the other one that poor Vix witnessed.'

At the sound of her name Vix left her pedicure long enough to cast a glance in my direction.

'Not likely. Just tightened the noose again. Let 'im choke, see.'

'I don't see. Why do that when he killed the other one so viciously?' It didn't seem to make any sense.

''E kills us for the skins. We seen 'em 'anging outside 'is 'ouse. All perfect they are. Even recognise 'em sometimes. That's why 'e was so cross wi' cousin, biting 'is leg off like that. Killed 'im in a rage and threw 'is body in 'edge after.' Rey looked round at Vix as he finished, realising that he may have described the event a bit too vividly, but she had taken it all quite calmly.

Watching her there, almost unconcerned at the telling of such a terrible story, I realised just how hardened these foxes were to their fate.

'You haven't been near the rubbish tip for a while, then?' I said, by way of summing up.

''E's got it ringed wi' wires.' Rey paused, looked at Vix and said, ''E's got some right tasty little ducks, though, ain't 'e, Vix?'

'Yeah.' She had slipped back into the old routine.

'Are you telling me that after this lad had set snares for you foxes, you have been down to his place and taken some of his ducks?' I was amazed to think of it.

''S'right. We do well off 'im, really. Got this little farm place down by main road, wi' ducks, chickens, sheep, pigs, bit o' everything 'e 'as. Little bit less now and then, when we ' ave bin around.' He chuckled at the memory.

'No wonder he tries to catch you lot.' My sympathy for the fox was dwindling fast.

'Don't reckon we does 'im that much 'arm. Anything as we 'ave is either dead, dying or downright pathetic. 'Tis just that 'e 'as more o' that sort o' stock than anyone else round these parts,' Rey said in justification.

'It would seem that you both probably deserve each other, but having nearly choked to death myself, I wouldn't want to come close to it again nor do I hold with thieving, so it would be nice to think you could both change your ways.' How absurdly pompous I sounded.

'Look 'ere mate. You live in a cosy little world. Your food's delivered to your nose and if ought goes wrong wi' ya, them 'umans comes to put ya right. You don't know the 'alf o' what it's like to 'ave to fight to live.' He put his argument forcibly.

'I'll have you know that . . . no. Perhaps you may be right. Let's say no more.' There didn't seem to be any point in continuing from there. He was set in his views, I in mine. I could have told him about the coal mine, the lonely winters at Pen-y-Bont and the hard work I had to do to get my food 'delivered to my nose' as he put it. Indeed, I could have gone so far as to tell him about my longings to be independent, to find my own food, with all day to do it in.

'We'd best get going, eh, Vix?' Rey got up and looked towards his mate.

'Yeah. Reckon,' replied Vix, at long last leaving her toes alone.

'Find a good spot to 'ide, lest your mates be after us today.' He glanced accusingly at me. With that they moved off towards the wood.

'Bye-ee,' I shouted after them. 'See you again sometime.'

'Ta-ra, mate,' was Rey's last word.

I watched them squeeze under the gate and set off up the track at a brisk trot, bouncing along in exactly the same way as Charlie did, nose close to the ground in case they were to miss anything worthwhile, tail slightly dipping to balance the other end, the legs moving with such ease that it was hard to believe there was any muscular effort involved at all.

In the intervening hours between the foxes leaving and Glyn returning, I must have dozed off again. When he did come to see how I was, he had Graham with him. Graham had been around in the woods all the time I had been at Barrymore. Not that I had had anything much to do with him, but he had unhooked me from a load now and then when I had been working without supervision, and had always had the time to give me a pat before I took myself back for the next tush. Now he came through the gate ahead of Glyn and came straight up to me with a mint in his outstretched hand. A big fuss was made of me. Both of the men looked at my neck and seemed to be having long discussions, whilst feeling and pointing to that part of me. How relieved I was to realise that, at long last, somebody knew what had been ailing me for the last two weeks. Graham put my bridle on but, mercifully, no collar, and led me out onto the same track the foxes had used. However we turned downhill, towards the farm. As we approached the buildings Rannoch cantered over to the fence to greet me.

'I was afraid we might have lost you.' He was very happy to see me, and his stride as he walked beside us had that bounce I had seen when he performed in the same field the other evening.

'To tell you the truth, it's good to see you, because I did have my doubts at one stage.' By way of reply Graham and I had a display of 'joie de vivre', as Rannoch put his head to the ground and tossed his mane from side to side whilst also kicking his hind feet high in the air, then to finish, he swung to look straight at Graham and I, reared up high, stretching one foreleg in a graceful arc to point at the ground in front of him as he returned to a horizontal position. Having completed this manoeuvre, he swung away to his left and tore away from us, leaving in his wake a multitude of divots hanging in mid air.

Although I am sure that my back would have stood his weight without any problem, Graham walked all the way back to Kit's field by my side. Whether it was for him to rest, or because of what I had been through I do not know, but whenever there was a nice piece of grass by the roadside, he allowed me to have a few minutes' grazing before we continued on our way. His concern, and the gentle way he handled me, made me wonder if he was to be my new handler. I sincerely hoped so.

Once he had put me into the field Graham sat on the gate to wait for Glyn. Looking at him sitting there, I changed my first opinion of his physique. When he had been leading me I had the impression of someone quite small by my side. I now realised that although short in height, he was very broad, with deep powerful muscles showing through his shirt, which was tight across his back as he sat hunched with his elbows on his knees. Gentle though I now knew him to be, he had a wild look about him, with his tousled hair, a head set directly onto his shoulders, thick leather belt defining a waistline, and his faded and often patched jeans, rolled up at the bottom to reveal his stout boots.

Once more alone in the field, the foxes over in Farm Wood came to mind and I wondered if Charlie would call by that evening, on the off-chance that I had returned, or perhaps he already knew I was here . . .

> We live in the wood,
> Badgers, rabbits and voles,
> We live by our wits,
> Foxes, kestrals and moles.
> We live without man,
> Squirrels, owls and stoats,
> You take from Man
> Whale meat and oats.
> You take either course,
> Cat, dog and horse,
> True freedom is hard,
> Survival by force.
> It's not as you think,
> Cat, dog and horse . . .

At the start of this recital I had turned around to see where it came from. There, sitting in the dead elm, was an owl.

'When did you think up that little number?' I asked the fluffy face some four metres above me. He stared at me for a while, then, after a slow blink, said:

'Oh, the other day, after your jaunt on the hill and when I saw this big black and tan dog hunting in the woods here. I don't think it had any idea what it was after or even how to set about it. Blundering around, crashing through the undergrowth, it was making almost as much noise as you did when you had that runaway log behind you. Stupid animal!'

'It's not that we have chosen a softer way of life, old Owl', I explained, 'there is more to it than that, which you probably cannot understand. But I will tell you, anyway. It is the sense of fulfilment that the dog and the horse get from serving Man. There is a definite satisfaction from doing things which, despite his supposed superiority, Man cannot do for himself.'

'Humph!' He shook his wings into a different position. 'I'll tell you what, I can hear Brock the badger coming down the wood. We'll ask him what he thinks when he gets into the field.'

I couldn't see the badger giving us the time to even venture an opinion on the subject. Nevertheless, as he came through his hole in the hedge the owl called over to him.

'Hey, Brock, come here a minute, will you? We want your opinion.' The badger moved on as if nothing had been said. The owl called him again, with the same result. Then, dropping from his perch he swooped by Brock's nose, coming to rest on the grass just the other side of him. The shuffling form came to a halt and glowered at the little owl.

'Can you spare a minute, Brock?' the owl asked with exaggerated politeness.

'Not really, but what do you want?' came the muttered reply.

'Well, we want your opinion to settle this argument. Well discussion, really, that Norman and I are having. Being an animal of undoubted wisdom, we thought your views would be worth having.' If the owl hadn't added the last bit, I think Brock would have gone, for there was a definate move to go when he thought he was going to be judge and jury in someone else's argument.

'I don't really get involved in other people's arguments, but what do you want to know?' he asked.

'No need to arbitrate, Brock, we just want your opinion. I was saying, that although Norman here lives outside with us, he is not one of us, for Man caters to all his needs. Feeds him when the weather gets rough, trims his feet and keeps him confined in this field. The same applies to the dog and the cat. None of them have the true freedom or the necessity to survive that we do. They are all but mere puppets of Man.' As if to signal the end of the speech, the owl fluffed his feathers and resettled them.

'You can leave the cat out,' said the badger without even pausing for thought. 'That's as wild as any of us; just picking the best place to live. Now, the dog is a pack animal but, kept apart from the pack, he will always be dependent on Man and, to a certain extent, that must also apply to the horse. But I think the horse is nearer the wild than that. Working for Man is a way of life for him, something that he does from choice rather than necessity.' He glanced in my direction for some sort of confirmation.

'Thank you, Brock. Just what I was saying.' As I said this he nodded a farewell and went on his way. The owl, too, flew back to his tree, clearly not wishing to prolong the discussion further.

My next glimpse of Charlie was not at all what I had expected nor I imagine what he would have wished. There had been many horses about all day. Some being ridden past early in the morning and others had gone by a bit later on in their boxes, similar to the one that I travelled in from Pen-y-Bont. All my interest in them had ceased though as it had been two hours or more since the last one passed.

At first I thought it might have been one stray dog lost up in the heart of the wood, but then I realised there was more than one up there baying. As I listened the volume of the cries increased and it was clear that there were many dogs. The excited pitch of their voices stirred something deep inside me. Almost involuntarily I found myself prancing around the field, all the time listening intently in the direction of the pack. Closer and closer they came. Now I could clearly distinguish between different voices. One of them, the nearest to me, recurred more frequently than the others.

I jumped wildly with fright as Charlie shot out of the hedge nearby. I hadn't even heard him coming. He was wet and untidy, his brush no longer clean and fluffy, but soaked and dripping with mud. Entering the field he shot away, then turned to come towards me, changing direction without apparently slackening his pace. Stupidly I almost asked him what the excitement was about, but in that instant, he must have known that I could be of no help to him, for he turned again and took to his usual track across the field and out onto the road. I shouted after him, something to the

102

effect that I hoped he would keep ahead of them. Fatuous, when considering that his life was in danger and he had a whole pack of foxhounds close behind him. I crossed the field to the point at which he had left and, looking up the road, just saw him turn sharply into the lower part of the wood.

The lead hound was quiet as she came into the field, but she must have been on the line for she came through the same gap in the hedge that Charlie had used. She had her nose to the ground and her tail held aloft. She moved in small sharp turns, always with her nose nearly touching the grass. As she did so she was joined by more hounds, all doing the same thing. One of them picked up some scent, where Charlie had come towards me, and giving a small yelp, brought the others to her. It was only when the same hound that had led them into the field moved further out from the hedge, cast about again, and then found the line, that they were once more on their way. As soon as she spoke, the rest of the pack knew her to be right, and, in a flash, they were all speaking behind her. As they were streaking across the field I found myself caught up in their enthusiasm and, to my horror, found I too had gone over to the roadside. Indeed, had there been no hedge I would have been out there with them, yet they were chasing my friend! Not only chasing but, chasing him with intent to kill, tear him apart, limb from limb; yet still, while knowing all this, I had a yearning to be with them.

The hounds were still on the road, having more trouble finding the line, when the first of the horses came down the lane. He was a large bay horse, big boned with a huge roman nose below wide-set eyes. Seeing him cantering slowly down the grass verge, it was hard to believe that anything of interest was going on at all. His pace was leisurely, but with each stride he covered an enormous amount of ground. As he got closer I could feel the turf beneath me shudder with his weight. On his back, dressed in a scarlet coat, his rider stood up in the stirrups, allowing the horse to rock gently back and forth beneath him. He held the reins loosely in his left hand, whilst with his right he waved the hounds forward, holding the horn in this hand as well. As he got amongst the pack the horse slowed to a trot, and the hounds ducked and scattered from his

path. When the huntsman passed them they would all look up in turn, awaiting some guidance as to where they should go next.

'Lew'n there! Lew'n little bitches!' shouted the huntsman, at the same time waving his horn to the right of the road. He did this all the way as the horse, now walking, moved away from me. Some of the hounds obediently took to the rough at the side of the road, but, without the scent there, they knew it was wrong, and soon came back out onto the tarmac again. Thinking he might be wrong he tried the left-hand side of the road, but this would have meant that the fox had back-tracked, and I could tell by his voice that he thought it unlikely. The hounds too understood his tone, for not one ventured off the road on that side.

Now the rest of the horses were upon us. In a disorderly mass, they appeared from the same place as the huntsman had done minutes before. Some were on the verge, but many were on the road itself. In contrast to the calm appearance of the old bay who arrived first, these looked more excited, the horses and their riders appearing to disagree about which route to take and the sudden appearance of the hounds in the road in front of them, making stopping a difficult but urgent matter. Amongst the front runners I recognised Cid, looking smaller in this company than I had thought him to be when we were together in the field. I made an effort to attract his attention, but it was wasted. Before long it became difficult to distinguish one horse from another, for now that they had all halted, a cloud of steam arose to envelop them all. Within this cloud they shuffled uneasily, impatient to be under-way again.

'Hike ike ike ike ike!' shouted the huntsman, as the same bitch spoke again, having found the line.

'Gi-awn, on on on! Gi-awn ma ladies! Hike ike ike ike gu-awn little bitches!' he shouted in encouragement.

That was it. All I could hear was the distant voices of the hounds, now fading fast with the deadening effect of the dense woodland. All the horses had gone, leaving only the white grooves in the road where their hooves had penetrated the surface. I longed for it to end. To see Charlie again, to know that he was safe. Anger welled up inside me at the thought of all those hounds and horses chasing the one small fox. All the more so as I tried to cover my guilt, for I knew that I would have been a party to it, had the opportunity arisen.

All day I expected to see Charlie come back through the field, prance across to me with his special light step, and nonchalantly say something like: 'That was a bit close.' But there was no sign of him. Some of the horses came by on their way home, but were too tired to say anything. Cid must have gone back another way for I didn't see him again either. Not for the first time, my field felt as small as the horse-box. A feeling of claustrophobia came over me and I had to get out and ascertain for myself what had happened. All that evening the regulars came and went.

'You don't happen to know how Charlie got on today?' I would ask.

'Sorry, no idea,' they would say in passing, as if nothing out of the ordinary had occurred. I began to feel that my concern was the only unusual occurrence and took to asking in a lower voice, forcing a casual tone.

8
IN SEARCH OF CHARLIE

All through the first half of the night I alternated between the part of the hedge where Charlie and the badger had their hole and the roadside, in the hope that I would spot him coming back. After that I started walking round the edge, looking for a way out.

The side of the field that abutted the road had the weakest bit of hedge, but it also had a strand of barbed wire running along it. The end near the shed was similar, but the barbed wire here was nailed to the small trees that grew in this line of hedge. On the opposite side to the road the hedge was thick but not very tall, whilst the remaining end went straight into a dense plantation of young trees, through which I could not have made any progress. I went round again. There had to be a weak point somewhere, it was just a matter of finding it. I went to have a look at Charlie's run. At least there was room enough to get my feet through. I tested the strength of the hedge by leaning on it. It gave with such ease that I had to put a leg through to prevent myself falling over.

Instinctively I started to pull back, but the thorns and twigs dug painfully into my flanks as I did so. I pushed forward, and with amazing ease came through to the woodland beyond.

Rejoicing in my freedom I trotted through the undergrowth to the path that led up into the wood, and then sped as fast as I could up this track. I bounced into the darkness of the trees, throwing my feet out in front of me, as I had seen Rannoch do down at the farm. It was to be shortlived, for the hill was steep and I was soon out of breath. I stopped in a clearing where the grass was both long and fresh. Despite the absence of rain it was soaking wet, and I now noticed how cold it was so deep into the trees. I ate for a while, and wondered how best to use my next few hours out of confinement. Who would best know the outcome of the day's hunt? Of course it had to be one of the horses. Any one of them who had been out that day would be bound to know whether they caught the fox or not.

Full of enthisiasm I went back down the wood, turning right into the lane, having decided to go in the general direction of Cid's field, but intending to stop and ask any other horse I might meet along the way. I had barely gone a quarter of a mile when a group of three horses came to the edge of their field to meet me.

'Any of you out hunting today?' I asked as I drew close enough. But none of them had, although they all saw the hounds, and were curious to know more about the day's events. As I related what little I had seen, their eyes lit up with excitement. They then told me how the horses gathered in front of them, listening as the hunt progressed through the wood, then shot off in the direction from which I had just come.

I moved on. The fields ran out and I found myself in a village. No sign of any horses here, only dogs, and the rustle of cats, as their shadows danced in and out of the gardens, oozing under gates or flowing over the profiles of the boundary walls. The noise of my hooves on the hard road sent the dogs into a frenzy. Feeling sure that the dogs would soon summon a human from his sleep, I took the first turning out of the village. The houses became fewer as the lane got narrower.

I knew that my field was somewhere to my right and that if I were to turn that way I should eventually get back there. At the same time I felt sure that Cid was behind me and that I should have turned left in the village, whereas, in my haste to get out, I had gone the other way. I therefore had to complete a circle to my left, unless I retraced my steps to the village once more, which I had no inclination to do. The first turn in the direction I wanted was not long coming. It was a track, and a rough one at that. Concentrating on the ground in front of me, for there were sharp stones that hurt my feet, I did not see the farm buildings until I was nearly upon them. It was hard to tell which of the buildings were for the animals and which for the humans, the two were so intermingled. An old pick-up truck was by one of the sheds, its open back half filled with hay and plastic bags, copious quantities of baler twine hanging from every point to which it could conceivably be attached. A hen threw herself from it as I approached, and ran with an absusrd lurching motion to the security of an older vehicle, half concealed under a growth of nettles. Simultaneously three calves pushed their heads over a stable door. The string holding it vibrated under tension, as the knot tightened with their combined weight. The six big black eyes followed me as I passed by them. At the other end of the yard stood a stack of hay. It had been partly used at one end and the bales lay at all angles, some reaching into the slurry around them. The faded green tarpaulin that had covered it now hung to one side, and the bottom two layers of bales had turned dark brown, whilst giving way under the weight of the others above them.

The track did not go out of the yard; only a rusty metal gate led to an orchard, under whose trees I could just make out the sleeping forms of a handful of sheep. I made my way back to the lane from whence I had come.

I did not have to go far before I joined another, wider road. Again I turned to my left. This time I felt sure that I would soon find myself in the area of Cid's field, and, thus encouraged, broke into a trot once more. A car came towards me, its headlights cutting a path for itself, and making it seem much darker than it really was. It slowed violently as it came abreast of me, then continued on again. The next car did not even slow down, but the first one to come from behind me stopped after if passed, and then pulled into the side of the road some way in front. The driver jumped out and placed himself squarely in the middle of the road. As I got closer to him he started to wave his arms up and down, like a goose stretching its wings. I could see there was to be no way of getting past him, so rather than try and dodge his flailing limbs I halted and weighed up the chances of getting off the road into the wood on either side. On my immediate right there was a big drop, too steep for me to go down safely, and what looked like water at the bottom. To the left was just thick undergrowth, with no apparent tracks or paths of any sort. Behind me the road wound out of sight, and in my haste to get to Cid, I had not taken note of what I had been passing on my way. I looked to the man ahead of me. His arms had ceased waving and were by his sides. I took a tentative step forward, which produced no reaction from him. Then I saw that where he had pulled off the road with his car, there was a path leading away from us. From a standstill I broke into a canter and went for it.

'Wow, hoy, stop! Wow boy.' His shouts were accompanied by panicked arm movements as he desperately tried to close the gap between us.

'Godammit!' I heard him exclaim as I passed the far side of his car.

The track was narrow and little used. Underfoot there was a coating of moss which gave a resilient feel to the weight of each step. The bracken on either side, heavy with dew, fell in symmetrical curves to meet in the middle, only to be brushed aside by my passing. My flanks were soon wet through from the foliage, much wetter than they ever got from the rain. Initially the incline had been steep, but it soon levelled out, and now quite suddenly I was descending. At the same time the bracken petered out; the moss turned to grass, and I found myself in an open area—no longer woodland and what trees there were, were well spaced out, and of differing varieties. Feeling that I had been heading in the right direction, I continued on the same line. But now there was no path to follow. I picked my way past many trees, all supported by timber stakes to which they were tied. Some were bare except for a small bunch of twigs at their summit, others curving over at the top and falling gracefully back to the ground. After a while the trees gave way to rows of plants, and a maze of small tracks.

Daylight was coming now, and I could pick out a line of cloud on the horizon. I could also see that I was in the midst of many paths, all laid out at right angles to one another. There seemed no obvious way out—not in any direction, let alone ahead of me, where I had wanted to go. It seemed like no time had passed when the sun made a small red semi-circle over the hills, and all colours turned to varying shades of russet. It was now that I could see that my instinct had indeed taken me in the right direction. Turned towards the sunrise, I could see that the farm, where Rannoch lived, was on my right, about half a mile away. I knew that Cid was not far from the farm, and rather than risk getting lost, I elected to go down and ask Rannoch how to find him. I was still trying to get out, when the first of the men arrived for work. Within a few minutes six people had gathered around me, all staring in my direction.

'Oh! It's Norman. You know Norman, from the woods.' The lady who had said this broke ranks, and came straight up to stroke me.

'Old Norman. Well fancy. What are you doing here, and what a mess you must have made.' Her hands were hard, like a man's, but the touch was welcoming and full of kindness. Someone produced a rope, which was just looped over my neck, and soon I was being led towards the farm.

Glyn put a proper head collar on me when we got there and led me to an empty stable. There was no welcome from him.

Mid morning, and Rannoch came from one side of the yard and passed out of the other. He was too far away for us to communicate. There was no sign of any other horse, so, for all my efforts, I was still no closer to knowing what had happened on that hunt.

Rannoch returned, still out of range. Hay and water was brought to me. Many men came and went, but I was ignored. Night fell and I slept soundly for much of it. Just after dawn the next day, the farm became temporarily busy as tractors were started and the days work commenced. Glyn appeared and took

111

me out to the field that I had been in once before. Still I was on my own. This time though I was able to have a word with Rannoch as he passed, but he hadn't been hunting that day and had no idea of what happened.

It was well into the afternoon when I heard the pleasing sound of hooves approaching the farm from the main road. Rushing to the fence I could see that it was Cid. He whinnied a greeting, at the same time showing surprise at seeing me there. Mark was riding him and brought Cid over towards me. Once there he dismounted, gave me a pat and tied Cid to the post and rail fence between us.

'Tell me about the hunt the other day, Cid,' I said, without even going through the usual pleasantries and, before he had a chance to reply, I added, 'Did you get the fox?'

'I didn't see you, Norman. Do you mean the day that we were around the woodland?' He didn't understand my urgency in needing to know about the fox.

'You and the rest of the field came straight past me.' I said, somewhat accusingly. 'In fact you stopped just in front of me, and the fox, a friend of mine, came right through my field.'

'Sorry Norman, but it does get very exciting sometimes, and I don't always notice everything around me when the hounds are running. I do remember being by your field though.' I could see he was thinking back to that day.

'Did you get the fox that day?' I asked again.

'Don't know really,' he answered. 'It was a good day though, we ran for miles after we left you.'

'What do you mean, you don't know? You must know whether you killed a fox or not.' I had to get a better answer than that.

'What difference does that make?' He looked puzzled.

'I have broken out of my field, come all the way over here, been locked up for a whole day and a night – all just to find you and ask whether you killed the fox that day; then you say what difference does it make.' Now I had got his attention I went on to explain in more detail.

'He was a friend of mine. Every evening he came through my field. Every evening he would stop for a chat. He used to do the same when Kit was there, he was a friend of hers as well.'

'I'm sorry, Norman. I wish I could be of more help, but the truth is that I really don't know the answer to your question. I think we did kill that day, but I wouldn't like to say that it was the same fox that we were chasing when we past your field.' I could tell he was being sincere.

'You must have some idea, Cid, you couldn't be there and not know what was going on,' I insisted.

'Well, I would say the chances are in his favour, but then they always are. Of all the foxes that the hounds get on to, only very few are ever killed. The hounds kill a lot of the stupid youngsters early in the season, but after that the foxes mostly get away. That day we were running for a long time, too long I would have thought for it to have been the same fox.'

'Did you stay in the woods all day?' I thought I would try and work it out for myself.

'No, from your field we went into the lower part of the wood. Very wet it was too. The fox, your fox that is, must have run along one of the main tracks. With the scent being very good in the wood, it was not difficult for the hounds to stay on the line, and the line followed the track. They raced on at great speed, and we followed as best we could. The horses at the front of the field had a clear run. For those of us further back it was not so easy. The leading horses threw up a lot of mud, some of which found its way into our eyes. But if you dropped back out of range, another horse and rider would come pushing past and take over the place you had just left. Then, of course, you had yet more spray and mud being thrown up. So we all kept tight together, so much so that I could see nothing but the rump of the horse one metre in front of me.'

'It doesn't sound much fun to me.' He didn't acknowledge this remark but went on with his recollection of the day's hunting.

'There was a slight pause, when we came to a big clearing in the middle of the wood. All the trees had been felled, in two large areas, and the ground was being dug out to a great depth. The hounds checked here, and we all waited for them to get going again. When they did, it was straight across the clearing, only to

113

stop again at an earth. When we got there it was obvious that the fox could not have gone into it, as it had been filled with fresh earth and sticks. The huntsman cast them around, and once more they picked up a line and were gone.'

'What if Charlie had got in,' I interrupted, 'he wouldn't have been spotted would he?'

'The hounds would have known.' He crushed any slight hope I had. 'If a fox has gone to earth, they scent him and start baying. This they never did. It was just that your friend knew of the earth, and had gone to it in the hope that he could have sought refuge there, but on finding it stopped, he had just gone on by it. The scent in the area though was strong enough, due to the earth having been lived in before, for the hounds to be confused for a short while.'

'It helped him get further away from them then,' I added, almost willing Charlie on his way, although all this had happened many days before.

'Oh yes, every little bit of deception helps to let the fox escape.' Cid was showing signs of admiration for the animal he chased.

'So you might just have lost him there,' I said. 'For it is surely possible that several foxes could have come to that earth since it had been stopped, and goodness knows which one you followed after that.'

'I know that you are hoping he escaped Norman, but it is all in the past. Whatever happened has happened, and I really do not know whether he is alive or not.' He was very serious all of a sudden.

'I know, Cid. It's just that I was very fond of him. He had been close to Kit, and that somehow makes him special to me. Anyway, you could have lost him there, couldn't you?' I thought he would have to agree.

'Possibly,' he admitted. 'But unlikely at that point. You get to know how the hounds work. What their various cries mean. In this case, once they were back on the line, it was as strong as ever, If it had been another fox who had been there earlier, it would have been different. The scent would have been colder, the hounds less sure of the line, and less enthusiastic for the hunt.

114

Their speech would have been different too. A few hounds giving tongue now and then, possibly not at all if the fox had left there some considerable time before. As it was they were soon back in full cry, and it had to be the same hot fox that they were on to.'

'Unless there had been another fox nearby?' I was determined to give him some chance at that point.

'As I said, it is possible.' He nodded in agreement as he spoke.

'You didn't see him?' I added.

'No, neither before nor after. I only had a slight glimpse of a fox in the distance, but that was later on when we were out of the wood, and it could have been any fox. Not that I would have known your friend in any case.'

'You have seen him before.' I thought he might have remembered Charlie. 'He was the one who came over to you one night with a message from me, but all you did was frighten one another.'

'Him! Well, I never actually saw him properly. And I certainly wouldn't recognise him now, and even less likely in the middle of a hunt.' He was right, of course.

'Please go on anyway, as I would like to know what happened.'

'Where were we? Oh, yes, we have just left the earth, and the hounds had picked up the line again. Well, they made their way back to the main track, and went straight down it and out of the woodland, running the lane for a short while, then turning into a large field. This field was planted with corn, so we went in through the gate. The hounds had scrambled over the wire fence. The fox must have gone under it, but the hounds being that much bigger, couldn't do that, and in their desperation to follow the line clawed their way up the netting, and then over the two strands of barbed wire on top of it. One of the hounds must have put its hind leg between the two top strands, for they had twisted around its limb. The poor creature was suspended by one hind leg, howling and snarling at anything that came near to it.'

How strange, I thought to be chasing something one moment, and then to be caught up like that the next.

'He looked an awful idiot when he was set free,' said Cid mirroring my thoughts.

115

'How was he released?' I asked.

'It took two people,' he explained. 'One put a hunting crop in the hounds mouth, so that he had something to bit on. Once he had got a good grip of that they held him up by the scruff, to take the weight off the wire. Then another person held the two wires apart and the hound was pulled free and let go. It was then that he looked so bashful. Instead of running off in pursuit of the rest of the pack, he slunk to the ground, ears flat to his head, and looked around, hoping to find that nobody had been watching. The size of the audience was too vast, and he set off at a gentle trot around the permineter of the field. He soon forgot his misfortune, and within a few minutes was back with the rest of the pack.'

'We had to go carefully around this field, so as not to damage the crop.' He explained to me earnestly. 'At the other side of the field there was a wicket gate, which led into a small bit of scrubland. Through this a path wound its way down a steep drop. The track had been used many times before, and went in a series of muddy steps. Between each tread we slipped and skidded on the damp slope, our hind legs tucked up beneath us, and tails dragging on the ground. Once we could see a clear run to the bottom, and the turf of the field below, it was safe to let gravity take over and speed up, knowing that the land further down would allow us to slacken our pace if we had to. As it was we didn't ease off at all. The lead hounds had gone straight across the cornfield and been quite untroubled going down the steep slope, so that they were now well ahead of us. There was a lot of distance to be made up between them and us followers. The ground was very old turf, ridge and furrow, which made it difficult to gallop over. It seemed that however hard I tried, my stride always co-incided with landing on the rising part of the ridge. At least we were going diagonally across it; for the way out was over a hedge, which the first horses were already lined up for. The huntsman was the first, of course. Jasper, the hunt horse who has been doing this for years, didn't even alter his stride. Indeed you would have had to look hard to notice that he was jumping anything. He seemed to just lift that little bit more as he got to the hedge, to carry the two of them over. The huntsman gave no impression of being aware that there had been a jump at all, concentrating all the time on where the hounds had gone, for they were getting ever further away from us. The rest of us lined up to jump in the same place, but when the little mare in front stopped, Mark pulled me out of the line, and we went over, just to the left of the spot where Jasper had jumped.'

He paused at this point; deep in his memories of the day. I chose not to interrupt.

'We landed in an orchard.' He suddenly decided to let me back into the hunt. 'No straight lines to follow there. We have to veer from one side to the other; changing leg almost every other stride, just missing the tips of the low-slung branches. Occasionally Mark would lie flat alongside my neck, hanging on with one arm cranked over my mane, and then we could fit under some of the taller trees. So fast were we through these trees, that we arrived at the rusty metal gate, on the far side, at the same time as Jasper. Mark and the huntsman said something to each other, and turned away from the gate. 'The hedge,' said Jasper, between gulps of air, 'go at it fast.' We were turning as he spoke, with Jasper a little bit ahead of me, and heading for the hedge to the left of the gate. I did wonder why we hadn't made for it in the first place, as it did not appear to be very high. Jasper, however, was putting more effort into getting a good run at this obstacle, than I had seen him do all day. Drawn along by his proximity I did the same. He took off a fraction before me, grunting with the effort as he did so. As I reached for the top of the hedge I could see the reason for his speed. On the landing side there was a big ditch, its sides steep and slippery. The vegetation was having difficulty in growing on the edge of it, making its appearance all the more menacing. I threw both front legs forward as far as they would reach, to get onto the firm ground beyond, bringing my hind legs right up to them for the same reason. Even so, as I thrust away, my hind feet broke the top of the bank, and I lost all impetus in the effort to regain my balance. Jasper, who had cleared the whole ditch with room to spare, went on remorselessly. My stumble must have been seen by all; for very few followed over the hedge. The gate though was difficult to open and from now on the hunting field was split in two, with only a dozen or less in the front group.

'You were lucky to have a warning of what was to come,' I said to Cid as he paused for breath, the pace of the hunt reflecting in his story-telling.

'Yes indeed, I would never have made it otherwise,' he agreed. Then went on: 'After that it was really good. Now that there were fewer of us, and all of them knew that each other could jump safely, there was no crowding at the fences, and the ground just seemed to roll by beneath us. I remember that there was a long line of new fences, all put in especially for the hunt, and easy to flow over. At this stage I think we did in fact gain a bit on the hounds, but before we got close to them again they went into a little piece of woodland. What went on in there I don't know, but . . .'

'What do you mean by that, Cid?' I thought he had brushed over that a bit too briefly.

'It's because of those moments that I cannot tell you whether your fox got away or not. I think it was almost certainly him that went into the little cover. But by that time the hounds must have been very close to him, and when they enter that sort of place they tend to fan out. It is very often the end for the chased animal, as he doesn't fully know from what direction the next hound is going to come. On the other hand it is equally confusing for the hounds, and I have seen a hound and a fox pass not more than a metre apart, and yet show no sign of having noticed one another.'

'So they could have caught him there.' I felt a slight tightening of my throat muscles.

'Yes,' he said without trying to soften the effect at all. I waited for him to continue.

'As we drew close to this cover, which all the hounds were in and around, we saw a fox leaving from the other side. It was only a brief view, and the only time that I saw a fox that day. Whether it was the same one that we had been chasing or not, I wouldn't like to say. I know that at the time everyone assumed it was, and the huntsman quickly went to the other side of the trees to lift the hounds to the fresh line. This they did readily, and took the line across another cornfield, and then over a big open drain, which was quite impossible for a horse to get across. The hounds were well spread out by the time we caught up with them again, for we had to go a long way round, following the tarmac roads. The majority were scattered along a main road. Lots of cars had to stop, and it was a question of everyone who was there lending a hand to control the traffic, and get the pack together again. Once we had achieved this, it was too late to start trying to pick up the line again, if indeed there was a line to pick up.'

'You mean that the fox might never have got to the road, or that he had just managed to lose them there?' I enquired.

'Yes, anything like that, or it's possible that the fox could have been headed on the road, and turned back into the following hounds.'

'Headed by what, they must be used to traffic and busy roads.' I didn't think Charlie, for one, would have been stupid enough to turn into the hounds for the sake of crossing a road.

'No, you're right. Actually a fox might well use the road to lose the hounds, because of all the strong smells from the car exhausts, which must irritate the hounds' nostrils as much as it does ours. But some of the people who follow the hunt, do so by car. These followers often anticipate the line the fox is going to take. Then, hoping to get a good view of it, they will use the speed of the car and the country lanes, to get well in front, ahead of the hunt. Of course the fox will then run into them, and, whilst he is used to seeing cars on the road, it is very different when he is confronted by a wall of people. As often as not, these same followers are so pleased at seeing the fox, that they cannot contain their enthusiasm. Letting out a loud yell, they then turn the fox back on its own tracks, where of course it meets the hounds.' Cid paused a moment, then, seeing my dismay, added: 'But I doubt if that did happen.'

I don't fully remember the rest of the conversation, I was deep in thought over that whole day's events as related by Cid. That he had enjoyed himself there was no doubt, and he seemed to place little importance on the life of the pursued and, at the same time, it did not seem to matter to him whether my friend was caught or not. To the horse at least that was not the object of the day's sport; but I'm sure the hounds would not have agreed.

119

Graham collected me from the stable the next morning as I had been put back in for the night. I don't think Glyn trusted me to stay on my own in the field. My mind was still very much on the unresolved fate of Charlie. I know that I put very little concentration into my work and may even have been rather obstructive. Why should not others have to share some of my frustration I thought, even if I had to create it for them. I hardly noticed where we worked nor what we were doing. My interest awoke only when I was turned out for the night. The field was entirely new to me, and, due to my introspective mood all day, I had little notion where it was. I could see it was well fenced, with barbed wire very much in evidence, and there was a shelter in the form of an old barn. Its roof had long since disappeared and one wall was merely a heap of stones on the ground, through which the nettles grew in abundance. The back wall was windowless but intact, whilst those on either side started at the full height and gradually fell away to meet the ground at the front. As I moved towards the ancient barn, a stagnant pond came into view beside it. A gnarled oak tree of great age stood between the two, its girth suggesting that it should have been of much greater height. Instead the large trunk held aloft a multitude of hefty branches, many broken and seasoned, the barkless timber a dull grey, but doubtless as hard as the stone of the barn.

The field itself was small, but ungrazed with a thick, matted carpet of grass. Beyond the barn lay a strip of immature trees, over which I could just see the chimneys and rooftops of a few houses. Most of these were now producing palls of smoke, rising straight into the dampening evening air. Although I could not make out the lines of the houses themselves, lights started to come on as I watched, and twinkled at me through the branches of the young trees.

As the humans settled into their dwellings, so the paddock came alive. It was as if there was more life in the vicinity of this settlement than I had around me on the edge of the big wood itself. The oak tree and the pond were obviously the first ports of call for many animals, my presence having little or no effect on their routine. How they watched each other though. Up in the tree an owl had come out onto the branch. Down below a mouse had crawled out from a crack at the base of the wall of the barn. A rat, its back humped up high, moved in short jerks around the edge of the pond. In the wood a pheasant called from its lofty perch, and set off a whole host of its kind in the same neighbourhood. I knew it must only be a matter of time before a fox was to appear. The area was ideally suited to their predatory and scavenging ways. Surprisingly it was not to be till the early hours of the morning that a vixen came to the pond. It was her lapping of water that drew my attention to her presence, for her approach had been so silent that until that moment I was unaware of her. I had been standing with my back to the barn wall, and my first step on the stones sounded like a landslide in the still air. The vixen, startled by the sudden noise behind her, leapt forward, landing foursquare up to her belly in the muddy water and now facing me, having spun around in her panic.

'A horse!' she exclaimed, 'a bloody horse, what on earth are you doing here?' Before I had a chance to offer an explanation she added, 'Why didn't you give some sort of warning before kicking the wall down or, better still, why couldn't you stand out in the open like all other horses do?' She shook her head vigorously to throw off as much of the water as she could, and then shook the rest of her body, sending a semicircle of tiny droplets around her like extravagant jewellery reflecting the moonlight.

'Sorry,' I said, but felt that it was rather inadequate in the circumstances.

'Never mind, with feet like that it must be difficult.' She looked at them as she spoke. 'Bye.' She turned to go.

'Do you, eh . . .' I started to ask, hoping that she would wait a while. She did stop to listen, so I started again, 'Do you know Charlie from the Old Hill Wood?'

'Sure I do,' she said with a low chuckle.

'Seen him lately?' I quizzed her.

'About a week ago. He was in a hell of a hurry though, didn't have anything to say.' She was having difficulty containing her amusement, though I couldn't see what was so funny.

Nevertheless I felt obliged to smile with her. About a week ago could have put the meeting either side of the hunt.

'Did you have the hunt around here?' I asked.

'That's when I saw him, Charlie that is. During the hunt. You could say he took over from me.' She laughed out loud this time, and I began to understand what her amusement might be about. It certainly stopped me from smiling along with her. 'Yep, they were hunting me you see. I was asleep in some bushes not far from here. The next thing I knew the whole copse was full of hounds, blundering about in all directions. I had to get out of there fast and silently. But once I was out in the open they were onto me. Close behind at that. I knew there was a dog fox near the edge of the big wood, for he had been barking a lot the night before. I went straight for him. I had seen him up there before, so I had a good idea that he would be in the same little patch of sunlight, between the start of the wood and an old water tank. The tank is set on some brick foundations, slightly above ground level. They are dry and when the sunlight filters through the briars that reach from the ground to the top of the tank, it is a warm spot and very well concealed. I passed by as close to the tank as I could, without waking him up, and then looked for a good spot to hide. I came upon it almost immediately, a drain under the path that led from this tank down to the first house it served. I could only just get in for it was silted up for half of its diameter. As I was about to crawl up it, Charlie came down the same path and turned into the wood itself about ten metres short of me. I don't know if he ever saw me but, if he did, he certainly didn't have the time to acknowledge it. The hounds came at the same moment, their howls seemed to be right inside my head, and the musty dry smell that goes with them filled the air. Shortly after that came your mates. They shook the ground like an earthquake. Straight over the drain they went. I heard it crack under the strain. At one time I was sure that it would give way and I would be crushed to death.'

She was clearly amused by the incident but I could not share her enjoyment. I was merely left wondering at the mentality of the fox, as she turned and trotted off into what was left of the night. Perhaps Charlie had later pulled a similar trick on another fox.

122

Could it be that the chase had taken him to another part of the countryside, one he had not been to before, and he was taking his time coming back or perhaps he just wasn't going to come back. I didn't know him that well anyway and my concern was not shared with any of what the owl at Kit's field would have called 'the truly wild animals.'

When Graham came the next morning I was resolved to make a better day of it. So we went back to work in the wood close to the paddock, a happier pair. Now that I took more notice of my surroundings, I became aware of the fenced-off area in which we were working. Part of the two-metre-high netting had been removed so that I could get inside, and it soon became clear that we were in a very large run, bustling with pheasants. They were as thick on the ground as any chicken run I had ever seen, and every bit as tame. I was sure that I would step on them as they pecked at the ground, seemingly unconcerned at my coming, only darting two or three paces out of the way at the very last moment. The fence encircled a patch of woodland containing a variety of trees. There were several mature oak trees, the tops of which were not clearly visible for, under their spreading branches, grew Christmas trees. These had now grown far too big to be taken for that purpose, and judging by the scars from the white droppings on their lower branches and trunks, they now served as dormitories for the dense bird population. On one side of the compound there was a strip of Thuya, spindly trees with thick evergreen foliage, the tops curling over as if unable to sustain the rate of growth and afflicted by rickets. It was these very trees that Graham and I were thinning out, for they were so closely planted that it was impossible to walk amongst them. As we progressed so another man, whom I had not seen previously, was erecting yet another fence, only one and half metres high, just before the start of these same trees. There were only the two of them and myself so that for a lot of the time I was standing idle. The trees to be felled had been marked by the removal of a slice of bark. Once Graham had felled them he would quickly trim off the side shoots. When he had prepared three trees in this way, they would be put into a tush behind me and I would take them to the track on the outside of the pen, where I waited for either Graham or the other man to undo them. During these pauses I asked the many birds around me about the fence and its purpose. 'It's to keep the foxes, dogs and cats away from us,' was the general sort of reply. The new fence was attributed to a second line of defence. Occasionally I asked if they were certain that it wasn't to keep them in. 'Oh no, after all we can fly out whenever we like.'

'Do you ever fly out?' I asked one splendid-looking cock bird, his head a purple hue with golden highlights and his tail feathers as long as his body.

'Not yet,' he replied, 'no need to. The food is here, and the water. The fence keeps the danger out, there are good trees to roost in, why go?'

Why indeed, I thought, although I was puzzled about the source of food. But not for long as, at the end of the day, Graham took me to a shed where the nearest good road ended; there he loaded two sacks of grain onto my back. These I then carried back up to the pen. I did this journey three times before all the food storage bins in the wood were full.

It was only a chance encounter with the game keeper's dog three months later that made the reasons for the new fence clear. It was the Christmas holiday, bitterly cold, bleak and damp. The sky was a continuous grey; darker by night and marginally colder, but little else to distinguish one hour from the other. A lot of shouting and shooting had been going on in the woods around me; now there was only the shouting as the party sat down to enjoy refreshments in and around the shed where my tack was kept. The dogs with them either sat and watched in anticipation of sharing in the masters' food, or wandered off to rest peacefully until further required. It was then that the gamekeeper's dog settled on some tall grass by the hedge around my field. To alleviate my boredom I went to disturb him and found him pleasantly friendly. The conversation soon came to the subject of the pheasant pen and I told him of my recent work there.

'That's the fence to make them fly,' he told me. 'They get so tame that when it comes to the shoting season, the silly things won't even leave the ground. I could kill most of them by catching

124

them up against the tall fence at the bottom of the pen, because once they get driven that close to it, it is too high for them to get over and they just flutter up and down the face of it. Now, with the new fence further into the pen, they have to take up the wing earlier, which takes them over the evergreens and then over the outer fence—after which they are shot at. If they don't fly at the first fence, they are caught and thrown into the air.'

'Quite a lot must get through the line of fire and escape into the wood itself though.' I knew this to be partly true, for there were several pheasants around the woodland, although nowhere near matching the density which I had witnessed in the pen.

'Most of those that do fly through the lines only work their way back again in the next few days, soon settling into the same routine. Then two weeks later they get shot at once more. The clever ones, and they are far and few between, realise it's no place to live when they get shot at a second time. When they get on the wing they keep going, away from the wood and the hills down to the cornfields below. There, they can spend the nights in the small covers, and roam the fields by day, which is much more natural to them anyway.'

Graham and the keeper were now leaning on the full bins, whilst I was waiting to be taken back to the field. The keeper then motioned to Graham to remain where he was whilst he moved towards one of the areas where the grain had been scattered. There he knelt down and threw little handfuls of grain towards a group of birds, while at the same time uttering short subdued whistles. Encouraged by the food and the comforting chirp-like sounds he was making, the birds came closer. Suddenly, with the swiftness of a snake's tongue, the hand went out once more. This time though there was no grain to be thrown. The hand opened and closed in the same instant, grabbing the unsuspecting hen pheasant around the neck. Continuing the same movement, the bird was swung off its feet, the body twisting violently in the air cartwheeled clockwise around its head. The wings twitched hopefully as if there might still be some escape from its fate, whilst the keeper walked back to Graham, the ever limper bird hanging from his right hand. With the aid of a piece of baler twine, that had

125

previously been tied around the top of the grain sacks, the bird was hung around Graham's neck, well hidden by his work coat. The two men exchanged cheery smiles and waves as we left.

Graham took me straight past the field in which I had been the night before. We went through the young plantation and out onto the road in the village, where I had seen the lights twinkling the previous evening. From there it was only a short walk down the lane to my regular home. As we travelled along I came to recognise this as the reverse of the route I had taken when I broke out in search of some information about the hunt and Charlie.

The three horses that I had spoken to that night were still in the same field and came trotting to the edge of the road in just the same way that they had previously.

'I see they finally caught up with you then,' shouted the largest one of the three. 'Did you find the hunt in the end?' asked the next one to him; whereupon they all broke into a rather forced laugh, while glancing from one to another to confirm the brilliance of their wit. Graham, meanwhile, was walking out at a great pace, unable to resist putting in the occasional skip, as we hastened down the hill. Clearly he was pleased with his recent gift which, no doubt, I had earned him by carrying the grain to those poor unsuspecting and very simple creatures.

9
A FOXES TALE

Did I find the hunt in the end? What a cheek. Not even very funny really. Certainly not warranting the bout of laughter they forced from themselves. Had I not been being hauled down the hill at such a fast rate, or had my mind not still been on those pheasants, I might well have put a quick end to their merriment.

'Look me up if you ever summon the courage to set foot outside your field.' Or perhaps 'What is it like to have a two-acre world?' Too late now though, but how nice it would be to be able to make such comments on the spur of the moment. It was some time since we had reached the field and my handler had gone home, leaving me an unusually large meal, as a result of which I now felt blissfully lazy and contented.

As usual I had no warning of his approach. Not the crack of a twig nor the rustling of a leaf, just the voice, as if he had been there all along and was now just continuing a conversation that had lapsed due to the lack of a suitable subject. 'You've been away a long time, Norman.' Charlie sat there, almost in front of me, just as he always used to. 'Norman, you've been away. Where have you been?' he asked, obviously thinking that I had not heard him the first time.

'Are you all right?' I asked without answering his question. 'I mean you are not hurt or anything like that? No broken legs or bad cuts?'

He looked up at me as if I were asking an incredibly stupid question, but I suspect that he knew full well what I meant and would rather I was forced to enlarge on the subject, so that he could play it down even more, like a brave and 'cool' fox should.

'Last time I saw you there was a pack of hounds snapping at your heels.' I obliged him to the full. He responded by pretending to see something at the other side of the field that had caught his attention. I thought of saying how downright terrified he looked that day, but decided to let him off. 'How did you manage to get away from them?'

'Not that easily,' he confided.

'I might as well tell you, Charlie, that I have been all over the county trying to find out whether you were OK or not. I expected you to return on the day of the hunt. But when you didn't appear I broke out and went to find Cid to see if he knew what had happened to you.'

'He wouldn't know anything,' said Charlie in obvious disgust. 'Did he know that it was a fox that they were chasing?'

'Certainly he knew. Not only that but he knew a lot about the hunt as well. He said he thought that there was a chance that you had escaped when the hunt came to the main road.' He sat impassively, neither confirming nor denying what I had suggested. 'Come on then, tell me how you did it. Where did you lose them, or did they just lose you?' The last phrase brought him out of his silence.

'Lose me? You must be joking. You don't get away from that gang so easily I can tell you. They may not be very bright, but with odds of thirty to one it is never a simple task to throw them off.' The image of the 'cool' fox was giving way to one of an animal fighting with its back to the wall.

'Charlie, I didn't for one moment think it was any other way, it's just that you seem to be so very calm about the whole episode

128

whilst I have feared for your life since you went out of sight over the other side of the road.' I could picture the bedraggled tail disappearing down the muddy track.

'Well, it's easy to appear calm now isn't it? It all took place some time ago. I can assure you that I was nothing like as calm the day of the hunt, nor for the next few days afterwards.' I could well believe him, and was quite relieved to hear this admission.

'Last night I met a vixen who said that she passed the hunt on to you, when they had caught her by surprise. After that I thought that I understood a little bit more of how you worked out your salvation amongst yourselves.'

'Where may I ask did you meet this vixen?' His voice had suddenly taken on a murderous tone; enough to make me realise that I may well have said something that would have been better kept to myself.

'Oh, back towards . . . eh, over the hill there.' Suddenly I was very much on the defensive, and in need of time to invent a suitable location where my informant would not be found.

'On top of the hill here you mean. Just here by the village, not far from where the hounds first found me.' He did not wait for me to answer. 'I wondered after the hunt how they got on to me so quickly, without me ever hearing them or the huntsman's horn first. Thank you, Norman, that does explain a lot. I had been worried that my slumber was becoming one of great depth in my old age, so much so that the entire hunt could be in full cry on my scent even before I had taken to my pads.' He paused in contemplation then added, 'I'll have words with that young madam later tonight if I can find her.'

'Perhaps I shouldn't have . . .' Before I could finish, Charlie interrupted.

'Don't worry about the young vixen, or what you have told me. As you have already indicated, such a trick is not all that unusual; indeed I would employ it myself if I had half the chance.' He gave a suppressed chuckle. 'I really was sound asleep when I heard the whole pack howling in my ears. It was hard to know whether it was a dream or reality, but I must have woken up already running. Pure luck that I ran the right way when you come to think about

129

it. No thought went into it at all. I would say that the first time that I was fully aware of my plight was when I came out of the wood into this field of yours.'

'You certainly looked a worried fox then,' I told him.

'Oh, indeed I was. I really didn't know which way to turn.' He paused in reflection.

'That's quite true, you didn't know which way to turn. You darted first one way and then the other. But when the hounds arrived in the field shortly after you, all your twists and turns had them thoroughly confused. It was quite a while before they picked up the correct line again.'

'Just as well they weren't too close to me then, a moment's indecision like that could have been fatal.' I could see that he was making a resolution not to leave himself in such a vulnerable position ever again. 'I did seem to get a bit of breathing space at that time. All the way through the bottom wood I kept thinking that I might have thrown them off. Many times I wanted to stop and rest for a while, but resolved to keep on running—just in case!'

'It wasn't just your line in the field that they had trouble with,' I added, 'they couldn't find where you went back into the wood. The hounds had to wait for the huntsman to catch up. He then took them slowly along the road, casting them either side until they hit the line again. It must have given you five to ten minutes' grace.'

'Then I wasted all of it.' He gently rebuked himself with a shake of the head. 'I had decided that I would have to get to the safety of a big earth. One where there were enough different burrows for them not to be able to dig me out.'

'Do they really do that?' I asked in surprise.

'Oh, yes very much so. It happened to me once when I was already underground, and a hunted fox came in to join me. He was steaming and utterly exhausted. Not long after he had come down the earth we could hear the hounds scratching and baying at the entrance. The noise was terrifying. It echoed down the chamber, producing a continual wail and groan. The whole earth seemed to vibrate with it. Then, as quickly as it had started, it ceased. Complete silence. We were even stupid enough to think that the hunt had gone away and left us. The fox who had come in to join me even ventured a short way back up the tunnel. Then I heard it; a scuffling sound and heavy sharp breathing, quite different to that of a fox.'

'No hound could possibly get down one of your earths,' I interrupted.

'No, Norman, no hound could, but those dratted little terriers can. If anything, they are smaller than we are and they come down to meet us. Then they yap and yap, taking the odd snap as well if we lose a moment's concentration. This is just what happened that day. The other fox must have been a brave fellow, for he never backed down the earth after he met the terrier, tired as he must have been. Just held his ground and hissed back, trying to get a bite in whenever he could.'

'Whatever happened in the end? Who gave way? How could you get out if your way was blocked by the other two?' I fired a multitude of questions at him without pausing.

'That's how I know about the digging. That is what happened next. It started shortly after the little dog began barking. Seemed far away at first, but each time the spade cut into the ground you could feel the progress that had been made. As they got really close it was almost as if the next entry of the blade would remove your head. Then, with one final slice, the tunnel was cut off. The other fox was still holding off the terrier but suddenly I could no longer hear what was going on. The silence was almost worse than the digging and the fighting that had ensued before. I remember that after a long while the spade was removed from the tunnel and a shaft of light came to the end where I was cowering. The human voices seemed to be in the earth with me, they were so close. I could hear the terrier sniffing about just above me, whimpering softly and scratching at the earth where the spade had been but he never came down and presently I could hear the voices and foot-steps receding as the group left.'

'What became of the other fox then?' I asked.

'They must have got him. My theory, for what it is worth, is that once the terrier was barking they started to dig a bit further down the earth than he was. Thus, when they got through to the tunnel itself, they would know that they had the fox between the opening and the dog. From then on it would only be a matter of time until they could reach him. I didn't come out until nightfall. But there was very little left of the earth and no sign of the other fox at all. But ever since then I have been very careful about which earths I go into and I would certainly not go into one when the hounds were after me, unless it was known to be so large that there was no way of reaching the bottom.'

'Where were you headed for the other day? One of the very large ones I presume.' I had almost forgotten it was the hunt I had witnessed that we had been talking about.

'Yes indeed, one of the very biggest around these parts. Used by lots of foxes and some badgers as well..'

'Badgers! In the same earth?' I was amazed to hear that these two might share a home.

'Well, yes, after a fashion. It is a vast complex of tunnels, all dug into the bank above a stream. The soil is sandy just there and us earth dwellers have been making homes there for many, many years. Now there are lots of tunnels, many of which link up underground. Nobody could have got me out of there had I been able to find a way in.'

'Cid said that the hunt came to an earth that had been filled in so that the fox could not get underground,' I told him.

'Well that must have been the one.' He went on, 'I spent far too long there trying to find an entrance that had been left open. Somehow when your mind has been set on something it is hard to suddenly change your plans. All the way down the long muddy track I had pictured taking refuge in this particular earth. There was another about half a mile away, nearly as good, but it was too late to go back there, as it would have meant going in the direction I had just come for the first quarter of a mile, and the hounds were already back on my trail. Stupidly I even thought of digging my way past some of the obstructions that had been placed in one of the holes. I was still messing about there when I realized that the hounds had closed right up again, and were following my scent down the line of the stream to the earth. They were coming on so well that I felt I would have to leave the wood, as the scent must have been too strong in there. My only chance, now that I knew

132

I could not go underground, was to lose them or pass the line onto another fox.'

'I know the hounds were checked for a while at this earth. They were not sure whether or not you had managed to find a way in, and then Cid thought the line might have got a bit confused because of other foxes having come to the same earth during the night. When he told me about that part of the hunt I felt that there was a good chance that you might have got away, and the hounds had taken off on another fox.' I waited for his reply.

'I wish it was that easy, but once they are really onto you it takes more than that to throw them off. I heard them speaking again just as I left the wood. In order to get out as soon as possible I went back to the main track, and then down that to the lane. It was as I hit the lane that I heard them start up again. I ran the road for a short while, but I know that they have the edge on me when it comes to a straight run so, at the first opportunity, I turned off into the fields. I saw a run, probably used by rabbits and hares, for I could only just fit through it, going under the wire fence into a cornfield. I started to follow the hedge around the edge, keeping relatively out of sight, but soon realized how futile that would be, and so went straight across the planted crop. At that stage I wasn't too sure of where I had got to, but when I reached the far side of the field there was a steep bank. It was covered in rough growth, small bushes, tufts of grass and ridged by an age of tracks running along the contours. Now I recalled where I was. Many times I had been to this spot, but never in such haste or from that direction. This was a chance to use some local knowledge to get a bit of distance between us. I flew stright to the bottom, barely touching the ground on my way. The hounds, I thought, would cast around on the bank, thinking that I would seek shelter there among the bushes. At the bottom of the hill the ground levelled off into old pasture and on this I was able to put on some good speed.

'I knew every gap in every hedge, even the boggy patches in the fields where the going would be slower. It was, therefore, all the more depressing when the hounds came over the top of the bank, and seemed to be down on the level with me in the very same instant. It could have been their cry haunting me but even at this pace and in the area I knew so well, they appeared to be gaining all the time.' By the tone of this voice he obviously felt that under those circumstances he should have been faster than his adversaries.

'You must have thought that you could not have kept them off for much longer,' I said, trying to picture myself in his position.

'No, I never doubted that I would get away from them, although at that stage it did seem to be proving rather more difficult than I had ever anticipated it would be,' he admitted.

'I suppose it wasn't the first time you had been hunted like that?' I asked.

'No. But on the other hand the answer could be yes. Often I have had the hounds on my tail in these woods here. But then it's quite easy to get rid of them. There are usually several of us on the move, all disturbed by the hounds, and the scent is very confusing for them. It's not often that they can hunt me as well as they did that day.'

'I am sure that I would have panicked and, as likely as not, run straight into them.' It was meant as a compliment to the remarkable way in which it appeared that he had appraised the situation as he went along.

'Well, you do have to keep thinking as you run: As I said before, numerically the odds are against you. However, the quarry does have the advantage of being able to make all the decisions about where the hunt will go, and you soon learn, as I have with the earths, where and where not to go.'

'Cid told me that you went into a small wood, and that although a fox came out again he wasn't sure whether it was you or another one.' As I spoke Charlie gave a short chuckle, then cocking his head to one side said:

'No fool is he, that Cid. Must have been hunting a long time to know so much about what goes on between us and the hounds. I never thought you horses had very much to do with it, just distant spectators tearing around the countryside not fully in control of mind or limb.'

I wasn't sure whether to defend my fellows or let the remark pass, although I had a distinct feeling that, in most cases, his

135

description was in all probability only too accurate. 'I know that he has been a hunting horse all his life,' was all I said on the subject. Then added, 'What happened in that wood?'

'Daydream Coppice it is. Well known to all the foxes around here. Probably the driest little wood for miles. No earths in it at all, the ground in it is far too hard. The trees are not very tall and the undergrowth is dense but somehow the sunlight filters through, warming the ground and making it an ideal place to lie up during the daytime. I would find another fox resting in there, of that I was certain, and just at that moment, that was what I needed more than anything else. A little bit of confusion, some space to plan a diversion, was vital. After entering the covert I went straight for the part I knew to be the best for resting in. There, as I had expected, was another fox curled up and enjoying a nap. Deliberately I ran right into him. Much the same as I had done earlier in the day, he awoke and ran, all in the same instant. Actually that is all I saw of him, for I never paused long enough to exchange a word. I left by the diagonally opposite corner, turned sharp right to try and confuse the hounds still more, and almost went back in the direction from which I had come.' He paused a while and then asked if Cid had known what had happened to the other fox.

'He thinks that they caught him whilst he was still in the wood,' I told him. As I started to speak, I wondered if I should have told a lie, denied that Cid had passed any comment on the subject.

'I thought they might have,' he said quite impassively.

'Don't you care that he died, almost in your place, as it were?' I asked him.

'Better him than me surely,' was the immediate reply.

'Strange fellows you foxes. You seem to have values that don't apply to the rest of us.' I knew I would never totally understand them.

'Anyway it did give me a little bit of extra time. Some time to plan things a bit.'

'How did you get them off your tail then, Charlie, for I know that they were still onto you after the wood.' I wanted to hear the end of the story now that we had come so far.

136

'Shortly after Daydream Coppice I came to a large ditch, too large to jump over, so I ran the bank for a short way. Evil-smelling water it had in it, stagnant with a layer of run-off from the nearby road floating on the top, giving it a purple tint. I plunged in and rather than crossing direct to the other side, swam along it for a short while. When I did emerge I had skimmed a layer off the top of the water. I smelt like one of the old tractors parked around the farm. Thus equipped I went for the main road, where I felt sure I would mingle well with the odours of the traffic. There were a lot of people there, all standing by parked cars. They didn't see me at first, not until I was right up on the road itself. Then they made such a noise, shouting and waving, that I changed my plan. I had intended to cross the road at an angle, hoping that in doing so the hounds would not pick me up again on the other side, due to the smell of the road and my layer of grime. As it was I ran along the verge and there, right in front of me, was the same ditch that I had crossed only a few minutes before. This was the point at which it ran under the road and where it collected the scum. With the ditch and myself smelling so alike I knew that I was now safe. I went down as close to the edge of the water as I could and slowly followed the ditch back towards the point where I had previously crossed it. The hounds all swam the ditch in front of me, then with great difficulty continued to hunt me all the way to the roadside, stopping to roll and wipe their bodies clean in the grass on the way. I couldn't see the horses at all but then the ditch would have been too big for them to cross.'

'You were lucky to get away so easily in the end,' I said.

'You make your own luck in a situation like that. The stream was there, and I used it.' This I knew to be true. Had the stream not turned up I felt sure that he would have worked something else to his advantage.

'You still didn't come back here that evening,' I half-heartedly chided him.

'No, I went back to Daydream Coppice and slept for two days,' he concluded.

We both stood for some time without exchanging any more words. For my part I was deep in thought about how the hounds had been put onto him, and also how he had tried to pass them onto another fox, although to be fair that was only diversionary and I am sure he had not intended it to end in a death. However now that he knew, he seemed remarkably unconcerned.

Charlie, on the other hand, sat with a smug expression on his face, reliving his brilliance in an aura of self-admiration. How different from the smelly, wet, exhaused, very frightened animal he must have been at the end of that long chase.

'Where did you get to when you were on your travels then?' He interrupted my thoughts. I outlined to him how I had broken out of the field and wandered around until I had found myself on the farm, and then gradually worked my way back again via the other wood. He smiled knowingly at my description of the pheasant pen, which was clearly a regular haunt of his.

He left shortly afterwards, leaving me wondering why I had been so concerned for him. Was it that I valued his friendship that much, or just curiosity to know what the outcome of the hunt had been? I concluded that it was the contact with his world, the truly wild one, that I valued and would miss dreadfully were he not to call by regularly anymore.

10
THE DREAM HUNT

It was a damp, cold and misty day. I could see the fields either side
of the lane, but beyond them everything faded into the same
murky background of crops and hedgerows. Our feet sounded
loud on the hard tarmac, only changing to a hollow, resonating
ring when we went through a puddle. Ahead of us were two more
horses, neither of which I had seen before. The one on the outside
was a well-proportioned animal, probably sixteen hands high,
pushing his body along the road with powerful strides. His
partner, inside him next to the verge, was a much taller horse,
totally lacking in breadth across the backside. Its motion along the
road suggested that the front legs were reluctantly pulling the rest
of it along. A hind leg was lazily dragged forward with each stride.
I wondered how it ever coped with going up hill.

Ahead of us the road narrowed, and a group of farm buildings
took shape in the mist. At first it looked as if the road was to end

with them, but as we got closer I could see that the buildings were all to the left-hand side, starting with a large barn painted a rust colour, followed by an open shed full of very bright red tractors. After some more buildings we came upon the farmhouse and, there in front, scattered around an orchard, were more horses than I had ever seen in my life. I never did count them but I would have thought them to number near one hundred. Cid and I went through an open gate and joined them. I followed him as I did not know where to go. All the others stood around, seemingly unconcerned at what was happening, although I did notice that away from the main group, one or two horses found it impossible to stand still, but they had been well segregated from the others.

We worked our way towards the middle of the bunch, where Cid stood beside another horse that he seemed to know. Presently two people appeared on foot, carrying trays, one with glasses of steaming red liquid, slightly pungent to the nose, the other with warm-smelling pastries. All around there was a lot of chatting amongst the riders, the majority of whom were in the customary black hunting coats. Many wore scarlet, more than I had ever seen previously when the hunt had passed by whilst I was at work or in the field. I also noticed for the first time that some of the black coats had different-coloured collars. Most were deep red but some had yellow, green or dark brown, and there was one coat completely green.

Mark, who was of course riding Cid, would occasionally move in order to talk to someone else, and each time he did so Graham and I would follow along and stand by his side. then suddenly all was quiet. The horses all raised their heads, pricked their ears and shuffled uneasily, pushing gently against one another. Someone in the crowd in front of us said a few words then the horn blew, some of the hounds barked or uttered a short howl at the joy of moving off and, as they went out through the gate, so the rest of us tried to do the same thing, all one hundred at once. Momentarily I thought of Hatty, the slender and fragile racehorse who had complained so bitterly about the pushing and shoving that took place during hunting, backing off slightly as I did so. Immediately three horses and a pony came between myself and

Cid. Frightened lest I should lose contact with him for the rest of the day I shouldered my way back into the gateway, joining the outgoing tide through the sluice-gate. Metal shoes slithered on the road as our rather stiff limbs were required to suddenly move our bodies at great speed but, mercifully, the snake of horses soon turned off the road into a field on the opposite side.

Most of the horses now broke into a slow canter, bouncing exaggeratedly high with each stride. Soon we passed through another gateway, muddy and slippery underfoot, but not so crowded. Looking up after leaving the gate behind, I could see that a wood was appearing out of the murk. Many horses seemed to be gathered as its edge, none of them standing still but moving this way and that, often travelling sideways. Then, as I got closer, I could see them one by one break away and canter towards the wood itself. There at its edge I could see them momentarily bob up in the air as they jumped into it. Although the number of those cantering towards it did not totally coincide with the number which appeared to actually clear the rails. Sure enough, when we got near to the front of the disorderly queue I could see that many a horse, prancing while awaiting its turn, would then take off at high speed towards the jump, only to slide to an undignified halt, its front feet pushed back under its belly, nose outstretched over the fence and tail horizontal in an effort to regain some sort of balance. The rider would be performing similar gymnastics in order to remain in the saddle and, subsequently, beating the hapless animal in a fit of frustration and embarrassment. Vowing not to be among the refusers I tucked in behind Cid and found that the fence was not very high and could be cleared with remarkable ease.

Thus delayed we were now able to canter through the relatively open woodland at great speed. The path was far from straight but the going was good and it was easy to maintain a fast canter swinging left and right around the trees and stumps; Graham occasionally taking a different line to Cid which would give us a view of the other horses in front. The steel grey in front of Cid was clearly a young horse, and every so often he would squeal with delight while giving a playful buck, allowing his heels to float over the briars at the side of the path. Then, suddenly, as if a door had been slammed in our faces, we came to an abrupt halt. It was like being back at the meet once more. No sign of the hounds nor any sound from the huntsman; I even wondered if we have come the right way after jumping into the wood. My concern did not appear to be shared by the others so I waited, as they did, in the cramped conditions on the path. When we moved off again it was as suddenly as we had stopped. Left handed and down the slope of the wood, fanning out and taking our own lines as we went. The density of the trees thinned, culminating in a shallow ditch, through which we all splashed at an unabated pace, thence to race up the turf on the other side and into the next field via another gateway. This stretch was bordered on the one side by an old railway line and, at the point at which we had entered, it was on a level with us. But turning left handed once more the grass fell away until the embankment towered above. The horses fanned out again and gathered momentum on the steep slope. At full speed I galloped for the bottom. The gateway was crowded to capacity once more and my kinetic energy would not allow us to stop without hitting the back of those already waiting to push through. Graham pulled me out to the right and I was then in line for the hedge, which was tall and reinforced by sheep netting and two strands of barbed wire. The adrenalin flowed in my veins as I resolved to show I was capable of clearing even this mighty obstacle. Graham continued to pull me to the right and the hedge was then alongside us on our left, so high that I could not see over it. We turned a full circle and made our way through the gate with the rest of the horses. Cid was waiting for us on the other side and said something to the effect that he thought we were going to attempt to jump the fence, laughing as he spoke. Looking back and seeing the size of it I too joined in his laughter, though it caught in my throat as a tremor went along my spine and down all four legs at once.

At a more sedate pace now, the hunt crossed the next small paddock before emerging onto the road and trotting past what had once been the railway bridge. A track on the left led to a small jump and, the initial exuberance now over, this was approached in an altogether calmer manner. We all cleared it and went on up onto the old railway itself.

The hounds were now busy working either side, the embankments thick and overgrown with briars and nettles, giving way in places to hawthorn, gorse and broom. Despite the hostility of the plants and the density of cover the hounds lost no enthusiasm for the job. With little or no encouragement from the huntsman they scoured each side, seldom using the old railway track itself to ease their path. I found myself watching each and every hound as it came into view, looking for some reaction from them to indicate that there was a fox in the vicinity. A slight movement of the stern; a double check under a particular bush or maybe even a slight whimper. Gradually we progressed down the line until our way was barred by a tall fence erected under the next bridge to cross the railway. The land on either side of us had risen so that we now had to climb out of the cutting back onto open farm land.

Several attempts were made to interest the hounds in the area around this next stretch of the embankment, but all to no avail. They knew very well that there was nothing lying-up there, and had little interest in searching further. The small paddock we were now in narrowed to a point, at the end of which was a gate and to the right had been placed a set of rails. Higher than anything that we had encountered so far that day, they caused a spate of refusals from the very onset. The huntsman himself was amongst that number and indeed it had been difficult enough for him to persuade the hounds to get over ahead of him, so that his horse could have a clear run. In fairness to the horse his task was a demanding one, for there were some hounds who steadfastly refused to go on ahead as they were bidden, therefore making the poor animal watch where he put his hooves as well as negotiating the fence itself. One hound in particular stood out amongst all the others; she was a pale-coloured bitch, with no markings on her other than a round black patch on her off thigh. Unlike the rest of the pack she appeared completely oblivious to the coercions of the huntsman, trotting around the edges of the paddock, investigating whatever took her attention at the time.

Gradually Cid and I were working our way to the front,

although the area around the jump was by now extremely crowded. Those anxious to get over the obstacle had pushed so far forward that it had to be cleared from a standing start in three strides. Those who had already been up to it and refused now remained within the same area, circling and twisting in a flustered attempt to realign themselves for a second, or third attempt. Cid and Mark saw the chance, a momentary gap. They got far too close, but rather than stop Cid sprang off all fours, like a cat mousing in long grass. The policy worked and I saw them cantering away into the distance. Now that I had been left behind I joined the group who were edging ever closer to the fence. I thought I saw an opportunity to go and plunged forward. Graham, however, had not seen it and unbalanced by my sudden move pulled me towards the gate. There we were to collide with a horse who had refused and was now pirouetting on the sidelines. In a joint mood of determination, Graham and I swung back to the starting point three strides out, then followed the next horse to go at the jump. As it refused and swung right, I put in one short stride and leapt. I must have got far too close, for my knees caught the top rail, forcing the whole structure to give to my weight, whilst at the same time checking me in the air and sending my jockey sprawling along my neck. We descended at far too steep an angle and, having twisted in mid-air, landed on the off fore only. Unable to take the strain this immediately started to buckle, and only by forcing my near fore to rush to our rescue did I avoid a heavy fall. It was several metres before I felt my rider had regained his composure and correct place in the saddle.

The leading group were now crossing a lane and entering another field. As I caught them up they started to jump a hedge. It was small immediately ahead of us but got bigger further to the right. After the last effort, I agreed with Graham's decision to get away from the mass and take it on the right. Big it certainly was but, having met it correctly, we floated through the air leaving the hedge well below us. Full of confidence I cantered on to the next boundary where a log nestled in a hedgerow, this appearing to be the right route to take. Checking our pace slightly we made our approach. The closer we got the worse the take-off area seemed.

Then to my horror I realised that I could not see anything on the landing side. The ground appeared to fall away so steeply that from four strides away it could well have been the edge of the world. Instinctively I started to come to a halt. Then at the last moment I could see that there was indeed a ledge of ground before it started to fall steeply away. From a near standstill I popped over and went on down the bank.

Fanned out to my right the hounds were working across the edge of the hill. Stems working hard and noses pressed to the ground, each one seemed to have a line of its own. Entering the bushes at different points all were gone from view. In order to keep up with them we followed along the valley, all the time keeping an eye and an ear for sight of fox or speaking hounds. One small hedge was jumped without any problem before a blood-curdling shout echoed down the valley.

'Gone away. Gone away!' shouted a mounted follower, strategically placed at the end of the gorse on the high ground ahead of the hounds, raising his hat high in the air as he did so.

'Hike holloa!' shouted the huntsman. 'Hike! Hike! Hike! Hike!' The hounds disappeared over the hill in the opposite direction to us.

Some of the field moved to the right, others to the left. The direct line to the hounds was impassable and a decision had to be made. The majority consensus took us left handed onto the road, from where we ran in a big circle, taking the first right-hand turn, bringing us past the point where we had recently crossed to the big hedge and drop fence. On down the road we slithered, turning right onto another lane, and then left into an enormous area of woodland. Then we came to a halt for there was now no sight nor sound of hounds. Whilst listening for them, one did appear, sniffing her way along the side of the track, unconcerned by anything around her. As she crossed from one side to the other I could see the one black patch on her off thigh. The huntsman disappeared into the wood, but the rest of us waited, with one hound, for his return. The cloud of steam that had enveloped us had long since gone, and a cold chill was setting in by the time the pack was reunited with us.

It was good to be on the move again as we set off for the next draw. Our route took us through a farmyard and then back alongside the railway. As the paddock narrowed I recognised the same large jump next to the gate. The one that had caused so much trouble an hour before. This time the hunt horse did not show any inclination to clear the obstacle and, much to the relief of all, the gate was opened for us to pass through. There was no alternative at the next obstacle for a hunt jump had been deliberately made in a wire fence to allow us access to the next piece of ground. Those ahead of us were starting to bunch up for the ritual push and shove prior to most jumps. Then I noticed that to the left there was an alternative. When the rails had been built, they had been put in at two different heights. To the left of the queue they were appreciably higher. In an instant everyone was on our right as we swung out of line, then seeing the fence at exactly the correct distance in front of us, I accelerated and left the ground, sailing over the obstacle to land well out into the next field from which a crop of sugar beet had already been removed. Despite the holding nature of the ground I moved swiftly and rapidly over it, following close behind the hounds and feeling that we had a right to be there at the front.

Before we had got to the far side there was a halloa from somewhere up ahead. The hounds needed no encouragement and soon had the line. Although we only had to jump one small gate, the fox took us for three miles, over grass fields, around corn, up steep banks and down through streams. He finally lost us at the top of a steep bank, where he went through sheep spoil and along a busy road with cars following the progress of the chase.

Tired but still in high spirits, those still left set off for the final draw of the day. This was to be a small wood; well planned for the hunt, as on all approaches there were jumps to give access to the horses. We had been over three of these, two simple sets of rails, one off the side of the road, and a slightly larger tiger trap, when two pairs of hounds strayed into a small patch of kale in a field adjacent to the wood. There only remained a small corner of the crop uneaten and I assumed it had not been considered worth drawing it properly. Almost at once a fox appeared from the tall

146

green shoots. He wasn't in any hurry, and we all had time to take a good look at him. It was the first time I had actually seen the hunted animal that day and I stared hard to see if he bore any resemblance to Charlie. He was not the proud handsome animal I had for a friend. Small and slender, his brush lacked the fluffed-up look of the large healthy fox. He did however have an air of confidence and took his time in deciding upon his line of escape.

Leaving the hounds still searching in the kale, he swiftly made for the wood. The huntsman soon had the hounds onto him, but the fox appeared to have the upper hand whilst he was still in the thick cover. Followers were soon on every ride and at each vantage point. Many times the fox was viewed and the hounds holloa-ed to the last sighting but, by that time, he was long gone and had shown his nose elsewhere. He did finally make for more open ground and was viewed away to the accompaniment of much enthusiastic holloa-ing. One or two couple of hounds made their way to the last sighting, as did the majority of the field, but the job of extricating the remainder of the hounds from the wood was not an easy one. Each individual now thought that he or she was close to the quarry and reluctant to leave. The huntsman and his whipper-in were becoming increasingly fraught. The followers started to gather from all corners of the wood, charging down the muddy tracks and thus ensuring that those hounds that were making an effort to get out could not do so. The jumps too were now proving to be major obstacles, the deep mud in the wood sapping the last bit of strength from the weary horses' limbs. Loose horses, their riders trudging wearily behind them, were now commonplace. By the time most of the hounds had gathered the line was going cold. At each hedge, ditch or change of direction they had to cast for the line. Since the fox had chosen to run parrellel to the route of the nearby lane, we made our way onto this and watched the progress from there. Occasionally a hound would speak, the others immediately coming to it, but the line was not strong enough for there to be any follow-up. Then there was a different sound. The fox barked. I looked around, but could see nothing. It happened again, quite distinct this time, and very reminiscent of the bark I had so often heard in my field. Still

I could not fully determine where it was coming from, but it became louder each successive time. All the hounds had disappeared. So had Cid and all the other horses. I became aware of a coldness creeping all over me. Then that bark again, louder still than ever before. Now I could no longer feel one of my front legs, and the cold became intense . . .

'It's dawn you know, Norman,' said Charlie, 'high time you were on your feet.'

'Oh, you are here,' I said rather foolishly.

'Been shouting at you for the last five minutes, afraid you might have passed on or something. Especially when I saw these marks on the ground around you. It looks for all the world as if you've been running in your sleep.' He walked around the brown lines carved out of the green grass, obviously made by my hooves.

'I have been hunting,' I said.

'Don't be so stupid.' He spat out the reply. 'You? The shape you are? Hell, you couldn't even leave the ground, never mind jump a hedge. Anyway you couldn't keep up a canter for more than a few metres.'

'Well, you are completely wrong,' I told him, as I got to my feet with as much agility as I could muster at that hour of the morning, then nearly falling as my numb leg failed to give the support I was depending on.

'Arthritic as well,' he observed as I hastily stepped aside to keep my balance. Then he shouted 'See you this evening!' and left without giving me any chance to explain.

As the feeling came back into my leg I eased my way across to the shed, where I knew the morning feed would come from. I really felt that I had been there with the hunt not just dreaming about it. I even looked at my knees to see if they bore the marks where we hit the rail.

I was brought back to full consciousness by the sound of a heavy padding coming down the path out of the wood. I moved to the edge of the field. There on the path by the shed was a foxhound. I was rendered speechless. The animal looked up at me, then continued to sniff around the shed as if in search of food.

'What are you doing here?' I asked in astonishment.

'Looking for a bite to eat,' she said without even turning around.

'There is nothing there except horse food,' I told her, then added: 'I thought you lived in kennels.'

She looked up then and told me how they had been hunting the day before, and that she had lost the pack. 'I've been in this damn wood all night,' she said. 'I'm surprised you didn't hear me last night. I barked and howled, hoping someone would come and find me.' With that she set off down the path towards the road, and as she went I could see that the only mark on the otherwise pale coat was a round black patch on the off thigh!

11
A STICKY MOMENT

I was to recall Cid's description of his reckless passage down the muddy tracks of the lower wood, when Graham collected me one morning and we took precisely the same route. Although it was during the summer following, the water still hung in places and there was clear evidence that horses had been on it. Each indentation held a puddle of water leaving the whole path pock-marked with mini craters. As I trod in these, which was inevit-able, a column of dirty cold water shot up, catching either myself or Graham, who was walking at my side. This all changed when we came upon a new road. Different to anything else I had ever seen in a woodland area. Large ditches had been dug on either side, and stone compressed onto the excavated soil in the middle. As we got onto this road I could see that ahead there was a much lighter patch amongst the darkness of the trees and, getting closer, it became clear that a large opening had been made.

Large yellow machines, jointed in the middle, with low-slung bellies, heaved their ungainly way around within the clearing. Shuffling over the uneven terrain they moved into the centre where, with a large cloud of black smoke, a layer of soil was scooped up from beneath to fill their cavernous containers. Once so loaded they moved to a line running across the centre of the valley, dumping the entire contents on an ever-growing wall. In the bottom of the valley ran a stream, which had already broken its banks, its flow interrupted by the quantity of earth ahead of it. On either side of the water lay a mass of timber and stumps, the yellow monsters working around these creating intricate patterns of differing soil colours and depths. I recalled Cid mentioning that he had come to an open area full of machines when he was describing the hunt to me. I looked around to see if I could spot the large earth to which both he and Charlie had referred, but there was no sign of it—just another large excavation of glaring stone and earth standing out amongst the subtle greens of the surrounding woods.

One of the smaller yellow bulldozers stopped pushing stumps around, and out of the cab jumped Glyn. Words were exchanged between him and Graham as well as a great deal of gesticulation, after which we set to work.

The object was to remove all the good timber from the clutches of the ever rising tide of water. On the face of it an easy task. The timber was not of any great size but the ground was becoming saturated and all my driving force was absorbed by the soft going as my feet sank into the mud, close to the water's edge. So we struggled, me with the mud up to my knees and Graham permanently wet. As day by day the water got higher so the task became more difficult. It was clearly a losing battle, for the rising water had already caused some of the timber to float. After three days the big machines pulled out, leaving Glyn, his small bulldozer, Graham and I on site. Glyn was totally occupied in pushing the stumps of the trees down into the water and out of view, whilst there was now a considerable collection of useful logs all above the theoretical water line. Graham and I were fully resigned to the arduous conditions and I at least was spurred on by the knowledge that no machine could do the job that I had been allocated.

Late one afternoon, shortly after Glyn and the others had left, Graham attached the sling to a log that was partly in the water. He gave the order for me to heave away. Leaning forward to use my weight to its best advantage, I dug my feet into the soft earth and heaved with all my might. The timber, being partly buoyant, came with unusual ease, to the accompaniment of loud sucking sounds as my feet pulled out of the ground at each step. Then it stopped abruptly. The sudden check caught me off balance and, unable to move my feet quickly to redress the situation, I stumbled and fell onto my left side. Immediately I tried to rise again but I could not get my legs beneath me, as they were still stuck in the mud in the same position as they had been before I had fallen over. Moreover the chains were still tight and allowed me no freedom of movement. Looking back beyond the chains I could see that the log I was pulling had passed beneath one of the stumps that Glyn had rolled down to the edge of the water with his bulldozer. This stump must have been finely balanced, for once touched it rolled over on top of the log, pushing it back and down into the water. Graham tried to remove the sling so that I would no longer be held from behind but, with the tension on it, he had no chance whatsoever. Remembering a previous occasion when the log had pulled me down the side of a hill, I was sure that he would now be able to come and undo the tack, just as Glyn had done once before. In fact he went for the other end, trying to roll the stump off the log, in order that he might be able to free the sling and take the pressure off that way. I could see the muscles beneath his rolled-up shirt sleeves as he gripped a protruding root with each hand. His feet were spread wide and, stamping them on the ground, he had made holds for each one before making a supreme effort to make the stump roll. It never yielded at all when he did apply pressure. Not being prepared to admit defeat he re-positioned himself in such a way that his shoulder, rather than hands and arms, was applying the force. Again he made footholds and, with his legs slightly bent, shoulder, head and neck all firmly against the root, he let out a mighty grunt. There was a slight movement in the stump, enough for him to try again, but I could see that it was all to no avail. I made a supreme effort to get back onto my feet, but found that all I could do was to writhe about on the ground, thrashing my head against the damp, cold mud.

Every time I lifted my head, in order to try and turn my body over the top of my legs, I felt that the movement sent me deeper into the mud. Not only that, but with each attempt I sank further so it became more and more difficult to rise again. Seeing my struggles Graham gave up trying to move the stump and came back to me. He grabbed hold of my bridle and by pulling on it encouraged me to try and get up once more. This time, with his help, I found that I was able to get my body upright and, as long as he kept the pressure on my head, I could stay that way. However, as soon as he relaxed his grip, I would immediately start to fall back to the prone position. It was still impossible for me to rise up completely or to move my legs to a better position.

There we were, face to face, me stuck in the mud and Graham supporting my head, and all the while I could feel the water was getting higher around me. Letting me fall gently back to the ground Graham then tried to undo my harness. I felt sure that I would now be set free. Once or twice when he stood up I assumed that I was no longer attached by the traces and so tried to rise. Still I found that I could do no more than raise my head and neck clear of the ground before gravity took over and I collapsed once more. I could now hear the utter frustration in Graham's voice as he shouted at me every time I made a move of any sort. He was pulling desperately at the chains in an effort to get some slack with which to undo them. Were it not for the effect of the suction of the mud beneath me I felt sure that his strength alone would have dragged me back towards the log. As it was, I could just feel the collar tighten around my neck, and the moment he relaxed his grip on the chain and tried to detach it my weight simply made it as taut as it had been previously.

His mood of despair turned to one of resignation. The tone of his voice no longer carried such an urgent note and his touch was one of comfort rather than force. I too ceased to struggle to right myself and in relaxing became aware that the wet and the cold had now reached the level of my spine, placing my nearside legs totally below the mud. Indeed it was now an effort to stop the water running up my nostril and I had to tilt my head slightly to one side to prevent this. Stroking my neck and giving it a firm pat

153

Graham got to his feet. He stood and looked down at me a while and then moved away towards the dam, initially breaking into a run, then stopping and turning as if to come back to me again. I whinnied for him to return and he took a step towards me but then swung around and left at a faster speed than before. He went out of sight almost immediately as he followed the contour around into the larger part of the bowl that was to be the lake. A few seconds later I saw him again as he ran on past the parked bulldozer that was on top of the dam itself.

Refusing to believe that I could be stuck in such a simple manner I made another effort get up. By placing my head and neck flat on the ground and then bringing it up with all my strength I managed to follow through with my shoulders, at which point I would be impeded by the tautness of the chains running back to the log. Nevertheless each swing got my feet a little bit further below me. I was sure that if I could only get to the point where both my front legs were directly beneath me, then I would be able to exert enough pressure to move the log and my body. Although the thought that this may not have been possible was at the back of my mind, I was not prepared to accept the reality of it.

There came a point, however, when the pain of exhaustion defeated the mental resolve. Continually trying to move my legs against a cast of mud had caused them to ache in a way that I had never experienced before. My neck, shoulders and lungs all felt much the same. It had even become difficult to breathe because of the water accumulating in the indentation made by my head. I had to rest before trying again.

Whilst struggling for air and suffering the pain in my exhausted limbs I found it difficult to even see what was around me. As the aches eased the whole scene came back into focus. No longer was there any panic. No shouting. No machines belching forth plumes of black smoke. Just all the animals going about their daily chores. There was even a chirpy little robin hopping on and off my back, plucking small insects from the mud oozing up on either side of me. Although I could not feel a breath of wind myself I could now see that the pale green leaves of the Chestnut coppice were gently turning back and forth on their stems. Higher above them the fine leaders of the stout Larch trees, tender and pale in comparison to the rest of the trunk, also swayed and twisted. Looking up, my attention was caught by the sudden appearance of a great number of birds overhead. Silhouetted against the bright sky, they wheeled and turned, sending a chill through my already cold body. They wouldn't go away; indeed as I watched, more and more came to join in. The whole area above the clearing was becoming full of these creatures, whirling round and round above me, all the time looking down on my plight which could, all too soon, turn to their advantage. I had even seen crows picking at the dead bodies of squirrels who had fallen victim to the motor car. How they would take a quick peck and instantly look around to see who was watching as if they were raiding someone else's store of food. How, when joined by another, they would squabble over whose property the carcase was. Would they really be standing on my back, pecking and fighting amongst each other at the same time as digging through to my flesh with those powerful black beaks. I shuddered in horror and turned the involuntary movement into another attempt to rise. More in panic than any co-ordinated effort I threw my neck and shoulders from side to side.

Calming down after this outburst I faced the real possibility that I would not be able to get out of this trap. I was alone in a hopeless situation and I could not see how anyone else was going to be able to be of any assistance even if they did happen to arrive on the scene. I though back to how Kit had ended her days, sick and weak, unable to do a day's work and knowing for some time in advance that the end was in sight. Hatty, the feeble ex-racehorse. Was he still alive, or had he gone the way that Cid had predicted? 'Just waiting until somebody . . .,' and there it had been left. What would have happened to him? Would a lorry have come for him one day, and, if so, would he have seen what might have been in store, or would he have just thought that he was going back into training, or moving to another field? Perhaps there was no caring either way, his mind conditioned and in-sulated by years of inactivity and negation. Yes, it was now many

155

years since I had come to Barrymore and I doubt I had thought of the little racehorse since I first left that field to start work in Kit's place. I must remember to ask Cid what became of him, I thought, realising the futility of that idea in my present predicament at almost the same instant.

As if to check that all this was really happening I looked up to the birds above. They were still there, but looking at the overall picture I got the impression that they appeared to enter from the right and exit to the left. I concentrated on one side at a time; and sure enough I could see new ones coming over the trees and into the clearing, while, when looking the other way, I could also see that others were leaving from the opposite side. I also noticed that those that left the clearing were at a considerably greater height than those who had just joined.

It was tempting to just ignore my observation. After all what could it possibily do to help me. Then again it was better to concentrate on something rather than dwell on my predicament; indeed I should be grateful that they clearly had no interest in me. Fixing my eyes on the next one to enter the clearing I could now see that they were not the vultures or crows I had originally taken them to be, but gulls returning to their night-time haunts, having had a busy day behind the plough or on rubbish tips.

As it crossed the trees the gull was in a shallow dive, its wings outstretched and steady, but once entering the clearing it had to move its body in a rocking motion in order to maintain the course it desired. A gentle flap of the wings and it entered into a spiral above me. Round and round it went, only moving its wings slightly to miss other birds on the same course. With each circuit it got higher, body and wings still inactive, although I could see the head constantly turning and observing all about it. What, I wondered, did they make of the dark grey shape lying in the mud below? Once high enough, a group of three or more would peel off and, in a shallow dive, head south-east for the Severn estuary. I wondered why they felt it was necessary to do that when they would inevitably turn around and return to the fields again the following day, especially as the ducks appeared to do the exact opposite, coming inland at dusk and returning to the river at dawn.

The water was slowly getting higher and I knew that I would be there all night. The sun had long since dropped below the level of the trees. The birds had taken on an air of urgency in their flight and the calls had a more positive ring to them as they all sought out their favourite roosting points. Pigeons came into the trees at great speed knowing precisely where they wished to alight, gathering in groups amongst the denser parts of the wood. The call of the crows echoed through the forest as they too got together in large groups, and moved around as a cloud, selecting their roost. How the sounds carried in the cooler air. In the distance a chainsaw buzzed, its note rising and falling as it chewed its way through timber. Now and then I could pick out the exhaust of a motor bike or a particularly noisy car wending its way along the road that divided the wood. Something splashed in the water down near the damn itself, where the stream had spread out, forming the lake. I could see the ripples spreading over the water, but no indication of what caused them. Another vehicle in the distance, this time more labouring. A faint rattle came with the tone of the engine, both partly muffled by surrounding trees.

My heart leapt as I realised the noise was that of Glyn's old Land Rover. It had a distinctive note all of its own, and I could now make out the unmistakable sound of the tail-gate chains rattling against the bare aluminium floor as it came along the newly made stone road. Onto the dam itself it drove and I called out in my excitement. Glyn and Graham both jumped out simultaneously; Graham running down to me from the top of the dam where they parked in front of the bulldozer, and Glyn getting straight into his yellow machine. I heard the 'phut, phut, phut' as it was coaxed into life, and saw the cloud of black smoke as the motor finally fired; the noise drowning everything else and echoing back off the trees, vibrating through the peace that had been.

Watching the cloud of exhaust rise slowly to the treetops I saw two ducks climb out of the clearing and circle as two small dots against the sky before leaving for a new feeding ground. Graham reached me and held my head in his hands. wiping the water off my nostril where it had lain against the ground. He was still in the same position when Glyn parked the bulldozer and ran down to join him. They briefly discussed the situation before Glyn produced a large axe from within the cab of the machine.

I could feel each blow as it struck the wire rope that formed the sling to the log. Such was the tension that I could even feel the additional stretch imposed on the remaining strands as it was partly severed. Then it parted, with such violence that my head was thrown forward to the ground. With pressure off the collar, the feeling started to return around my shoulder and with it the pain that, until then, had been numbed. Glyn took what was left of the sling whilst Graham pulled on the bridle. This time, with their help, I got onto my front legs, and when they changed the direction of pull to the front, I was able to rise completely, although my feet were still buried deep in the mud. Still they shouted and pulled, urging me all the time to walk out of the pit that I had created for myself. There was not an ounce of feeling in any of my legs and although I could stand, albeit with a slight sway, any further movement had to wait. Unaware of my plight both of them set to work with spade and bare hands to remove the worst of the clinging earth from around my feet. To such good effect did they do this that when I felt able to make another try, I extricated myself with comparative ease. The joy shown by the two men was only exceeded by my relief and gratitude, although I did not know how to put expression to either.

Graham and I were to spend many more days working at the site of these two lakes, but from that day on we worked with much more caution and, if it looked at if a piece of timber was too close to the water's edge, it was left to be retrieved at a later date, once it had floated down to the dam.

I remember one particular day when the first batch of fish arrived. Graham was summoned to help with transporting them from the tank on the back of a small truck, into the water itself. Whilst this was going on I was tied to a tree nearby which afforded a good view of the proceedings.

Once the tanks had been partially drained of water the fish were scooped out by the netful. Each net was emptied into a large black bucket and this was then taken to the water's edge, where the contents were very gently tipped into the water. Some of the fish were quite dopey and fell into the lake, where they lay on their sides, looking very dead. Others seemed too frisky and, as the water flowed gently from the bucket, they insisted on attempting to swim upstream within the fast draining container. It was amazing how they could use a mere trickle of water to make progress against it. When these hit the water they continued in the same direction, thus, instead of going out into the middle of the lake, they immediately found themselves stranded on the sloping edge of the dam. Once all the fish had been moved it was necessary for everyone to search the water's edge for those that were still stranded. No easy task now that the water had been disturbed and become rust red in colour. Made fully aware of their freedom the fish raced into the deeper water, and could be seen jumping clear of the surface out in the middle of the lake.

A regular visitor to the site was a large black dog. She came with Cid's owner, either following behind the horse, or if her master came by car, she would be inside with him. No sooner out the car she would be in the water. Not just on the edge but right out into the middle, swimming strongly. Initially she used to wait around for a piece of wood to be thrown in for her to retrieve, but she soon became aware of the multitude of timber and debris already on the water, and then made it her duty to clear the whole area, single-handed. For hours at a time you could look over to the water and see this black dog either struggling in the middle of the lake with a piece of timber four times her size, or attempting to pull it up the bank, clear of the water.

Whilst the fish were being unloaded she had been sensibly shut away in the back of a car, but from there had watched every detail of the proceedings and with a very definite interest. Long after the last fish had been coaxed away from the bank she was allowed loose. At once she plunged into the water. Every fish that jumped was a new target. It was doubtful that she would ever leave the water so long as the fish kept rising. Once the truck had gone we all returned to work and little attention was paid to the dog swimming around in the middle. What was noticed some time later on, was that the dog was no longer swimming, but now lay on the edge of the dam eating! Graham was first on the scene and shouted to the others to come and look, for there the dog lay chewing her way through one of the larger trout that had recently been delivered. Needless to say she did not take kindly to any attempts that were made to remove it from her and she was thus allowed to finish her meal in peace. After that day no more logs were pulled out by the dog. She just patrolled the shore, and should any fish be seen to rise she would leap into the water and swim for the centre of the ripples. Whether she had had the good luck to have caught the fish in the water or whether it was one that had been missed on the edge I don't know, but it was only live objects that interested her from then on.

As the shores around the lakes healed from the work that had been going on, so the population increased. Many animals that would not normally reside in a wood appeared, some quite bold and unafraid that they could be seen and heard at any time of the day. Others were nocturnal and I only knew of their presence by hearing them pass or being told by a third party. Many coots and moorhens moved in with the water. It was almost as if they had been there ready to float downstream. Whenever we turned up for work in the morning they would be out on the lake, but as soon as we arrived they hid in the bushes or dived under the water, emerging after a few minutes when they had got used to our presence. Occasionally a water rat would be disturbed as I walked around the water's edge. If there were no obvious hiding place on land it would plop into the water and swim away with great dexterity; little more than a small wake to show where it was. In winter the duck were to visit in great numbers. Just after dusk I would hear them from my field, calling to one another as they flew in from the river. I seldom saw them and if they did not call I could still hear the rush of air from their wings as they came low over the field, circling prior to landing.

The one bird that never made any sound, but whom I saw frequently, was a heron. Long before we ever reached the lakes in the morning, even when we were so far away that you would have thought it was impossible for him to have been aware of our approach, I would see his shadowy figure climb gently, but with

160

great rapidity, away from the water's edge and out of sight. He was the most subtle of thieves and I doubt that the humans were ever aware of his continual presence. Charlie, who in time, also developed a taste for fish, told me how he would hide and watch this master fisherman; the heron. Standing well out in the water, waiting, completely motionless, until his prey came well within striking distance. Then, with a movement hard to follow due to its speed, the unsuspecting fish would be caught in his beak. At this point Charlie would make a lot of noise and plunge towards the bird, hoping either to catch both it and the fish, or at least frighten it into dropping the fish for him to consume. It never worked, for he told me how the heron would gently spread his wings, then as if by magic, simply float high above the water and away. Charlie's only fish dinner came from those that, for one reason or another, happened to die and get washed to the water's edge; this was a frequent event especially after a fresh delivery.

12
OUT OF COMMISSION

One day, it occurred to me how long I must have been at Barrymore, for I was taken back to the first patch of Christmas trees I had worked in after my arrival. At that time the trees were small, ranging from three to six feet, and although they must have been present I do not recall seeing any forest trees at all, only acres and acres of Spruce. Now we had come back to help with the first thinning of the forest crop. The Christmas trees were few and far between. Those that did remain were the poor specimens; unable to grow with any uniformity they had been bypassed in each successive cropping. Now, totally outspaced by the more virile trees around them, they took on a sad brown tint as they suffocated from lack of light. The whole forestry compartment that I remembered being full of gulleys and mounds was already taking on a level appearance. Two large Redwood trees had been left, and when I had last been there these two giants had stood proudly over their younger brethren. Now, one had fallen whilst the other, suddenly exposed after a life of shelter in the midst of the wood, had bent and withered – its leader broken out of the top by the voilent force of the winds, a monument to the vandalism of nature.

The work was easy this time. The trees were still so small that there was no great weight to them, and each tush was of necessity small to avoid damaging the other trees around. It was satisfying to come each morning and walk into the wood, passing the area we had cleared in the previous days; turning a chaotic growth of conifer and coppicing hardwood into well-defined rows. Although I knew that they would have to be thinned out a further ten times before the whole area was felled to begin the cycle once more. As fast as Graham and I were getting the tree lengths to the ride-side, another gang would be following behind, making them into fencing stakes.

Many days we had been working in the same patch and it had become routine to all of us. The men must have been earning good wages in the easy going, for they were happy, jolly and cheerful. We had just had a short break for lunch and had got back to work as keen as ever. The tush had been affixed behind me and I set off for the ride ahead. The four small trunks followed me with ease and I maintained a fast walk in case there was any resistance along the way. A slight dip in the ground ahead made me put in an extra pull. As it levelled out again I felt my front foot sink into a burrow. Before I could check myself I had stumbled as I dragged my weight out of the rabbits' front door. The alleyway we had made for ourselves to work in was narrow and this slight deviation was enough to send me into the tree on my left, which I hit hard with my shoulder, coming to a very abrupt halt. A tingling sensation ran from the crest of my neck, through the shoulder itself, and on down to my hoof. Concentrating in the shoulder a moment later, it was as if a red hot knife had been thrust into me. I remained completely stationary, more in amazement at the severity of the pain than for any other reason. It seemed totally out of proportion to what had just happened. Graham came to my head, gave me a pat on the neck and went to help guide me round the tree. By this time I had lost all feeling in that leg—I just could not move from where I was. Graham made several more attempts to get me to move, but he knew that something was wrong, for he did not try very hard—there was more hope than force in his touch.

Resigned to the fact that I had sustained some form of injury, Graham detached the timber from behind me, folded the chains over my back, and tried again to get me to follow him out of the wood. By now sensation had returned to the leg and shoulder, but I found that the pain was only bearable if I held the leg slightly forward with no weight on the flat of my hoof. I tried to move but the pain made any further manoeuvre out of the question. Graham looked at the leg, ran his fingers all down my tendons, and then examined my foot. He took out a small knife, and clearing the mud from the sole studied the base of the hoof most thoroughly. I knew that he was completely puzzled by my injury. Once more he tugged at my bridle and offered encouraging sounds whilst so doing. I took one tentative step, hopping on my sound front leg and dragging the other, then I did the same again, but the pain was such that I then refused to move any further. Realising that the battle was lost, Graham tied me to the nearest tree and left to fetch help and guidance as to what should be done.

I soon found that, as long as I did not make any effort to move, and could maintain the one position, there was next to no pain at all. There I remained, tied to a tree in the middle of the wood, hoping fervently that I would be able to stay there until the shoulder improved.

My heart sank at the sound of human voices approaching from the direction of the main track. Graham came into sight first, followed by a woman whom I had not seen before, and Glyn at the back. They stood around me while Graham explained what had happened, going back to where the hole was, and then indicating the offending tree. Glyn surveyed Graham and me with obvious displeasure, no doubt already wondering how he was going to get all this timber out of the wood without the help of a horse. The lady stood close to my head, near enough for my nostrils to pick up the acrid smell of stale sweat. Her hair was dark, but streaked with grey, short cropped and clinging closely to the contours of her scalp. Whilst her hair showed the contours of her head so her tight-fitting dark brown breeches showed the outline lower down, which was no more sightly than that above, although a large baggy jersey, with holes in the sleeves did its best to hide the largest part of the quarters. Her boots were stained by years of horse muck and crumbling around the inner calf from contact with the saddle. Whilst listening to Graham's account of what had happened, she reached out towards my muzzle and I could not help but recoil from her touch. As if my moving away from her had been a grave error on my part, she now ignored what was being said and advanced upon me, determined that I should appear friendly towards her and not flinch in fright. Under the circumstances, there was nothing I could do, but I would have dearly loved to have been able to run away. Again my leg was inspected in minute detail; every tendon and joint as well as the inside of the hoof. The leg was pulled forward and back by this imposing woman and, with each new line of investigation, Graham and Glyn seemed to be subjected to a long and detailed lecture. With much cajoling I was made to take a further two steps for her benefit, whereupon she whooped with delight and went back to investigating the underside of my foot. This went on for some time before it was evidently decided that I would have to make my own way back up to the track.

I got there by swinging my bad leg forward so that its momentum carried it well in front of me. However hard I tried not to put any weight on the bad leg, the rough going made this virtually impossible and at times my injured limb would be caught in mid swing by a bush, stump or tuft of grass. Such moments were excruciatingly painful. Getting to the track was a major achievement and there was no chance of them getting me to go on after that. Correctly assessing the situation Glyn left to get some transport, whilst Graham remained with me. The woman, who had seemingly been brought in to diagnose my injuries, regrettably stayed also and, not content with her previous analysis, proceeded to push and prod further, often looking at the same joint or tendon again and again while subjecting Graham to an ongoing lecture.

How I managed to get up the ramp into the trailer when it arrived I shall never know although, at the time, it was the lesser of two evils; the trailer or still more diagnosis. During the actual travelling I was able to keep any weight off the leg so the discomfort was minimal, and backing out at the other end proved to be simplicity itself as I merely dragged the offending foot as I backed out.

I had not however been brought to my own field. It took me a while to recognise the stable yard—the tree growing out of the wall on the left, and the large stables with cast-iron railings topping the planked divisions. It was where I had had my first view of Barrymore. I dragged myself gratefully through the stable door that was held open for me, and did my best to relax. We did at least appear to have thrown off the amateur vet, and for a period I was left in complete peace.

It was already dark when Mark arrived at the stables. He looked at me over the stable door and then came in and went through the now standard routine examination; leg, tendons and foot. How I wished I could explain where the pain was! After his examination of my leg Mark went to the next-door stable and started to make it up before bringing Cid in for the night. Mark was partway to the field to get him when a car's headlights scythed up towards the two stables. It continued at an unabated speed to within a few metres of the door itself, before coming to an abrupt halt. Even before it had settled on its springs the driver jumped out, causing the car to rise dramatically with the loss of weight. Without shutting the door, he advanced towards the stable, sleeves rolled up, tie loose around his neck, a squat purposeful figure of a man. Straight into the stable he came, stood broadside to me and just looked for a moment. He then made me take a step forward by patting my rump purposefully. Moving to my head he then pushed me back one step. By this time Mark had returned but the new arrival did not seem to acknowledge his presence. A quick look at the inside of my hoof seemed to confirm his original diagnosis that it had nothing whatever to do with my difficulty. He then put a hand on my shoulder while, at the same time, turning to Mark and explaining what the problem was likely to be. Shouting some instructions as he got back into the car he was on his way again so quickly that it was hardly possible to be sure that I hadn't imagined the whole visit. A disconsolate Mark set off once more to get his horse.

'That looks worse than it sounds,' said Cid later, as I shuffled my way across the stable to get to the hay net that Mark had just placed in there for me. 'Long old job, getting a shoulder right again,' he went on. 'Reckon you won't be in work for a long, long time. Saw a horse crash into a tree out hunting once; he dragged his leg just like you, but I haven't seen him since, and he used to be out with us regularly—so it must be a protracted cure.' He rambled on about crashes and injuries sustained by various friends and acquaintances but I was in no mood for such idle conversation and said nothing myself, although I was very glad to have his company, for what might well have been a long, cold, painful night passed away with surprising ease.

For the next five days I was to stay in the stable. Each night Cid would be collected from the field, and brought in to join me. Thus it was the days that seemed to drag. I wondered how so many horses managed to live in a stable all their working lives, and not go crazy with the boredom of it. Every morning Graham would come to the stable and clean it out, putting down some fresh straw, hay and water and each evening Mark would do much the same when he tended Cid. The big excitement for Cid was when he was brought in, but instead of being bedded down for the night, the brushes came out and he was given a thorough grooming. This was the signal that tomorrow would be a hunting day. It also turned out to be a signal that tonight would be a restless one. If ever I doubted how much it meant to that horse to go hunting, those doubts were dispelled through that one night.

When the green canvas rug came off, he got a thorough grooming all over with brushes, then, after that, a suction machine would be used on his neck., back and rump. This was followed by a shampoo of his mane and tail, the tail then being bound in a bandage. His three white socks would be the final part to receive a wash and dry. I was amazed and speechless to witness this complicated procedure. The small black pony-like figure, covered in mud, that had come up to the stables an hour earlier was transformed. Clods of mud had hung in his mane and tail—they now gleamed like silk. His white blaze and star had been dull and stained, not the radiant white they now were. His coat had had a dull, matt appearance but that too had a deep shine to it. Cid looked as good as any thoroughbred I had ever seen. Gone was any similarity between himself and a pony; he had been changed into a grand and noble horse, of that there was no doubt.

Just after Cid and his master had got into their transport next morning to go to the meet, Glyn came to take me out of the stable. It was a great relief to be getting out into the fresh air again and I now found that I could move at quite a respectable pace by swinging my leg forward. We didn't have to go far. Down the lane a short way, past the entrance to the top field, where I had gone that first day, and then in through the first gateway on the left, into what was the lower field—where Kit had been put the first time I saw her all those years before. Although it had been a walk of only two to three hundred metres, I was completely out of breath and had to stand a while in the gateway before attempting to move further into the field itself. Still puffing I was glad to see that I was not to be alone. A large bright bay horse was making slow progress across the grass towards me.

'Cid told me you were up in the stables with him,' said Mole as he came within earshot. 'Some sort of accident I believe.' I told him the details of what had happened that day, to which he listened sympathetically. Slowly we grazed our way into the middle of the field. The fresh grass was sharp and succulent after the enforced diet of hay that I had suffered over the last five days.

My muzzle was still on the ground making the most of the grazing, when I noticed one of Mole's front legs. I stopped munching but kept my head lowered to get a good look. From the knee down to the fetlock there was hardly any hair at all. Instead there was a series of black patches, interspersed with what looked to be fresh sores. As I brought my head up I met his gaze, eye to eye for he had been watching me study his leg.

'Not a pretty sight is it?' he said, after a pause.

'It looks extremely painful,' I replied.

'It was,' he said with obvious relief. 'Much better now though, but it was agony when they first did it.'

'They did it? Do you mean that it was deliberate?' I could not conceal my surprise.

'Oh yes, very deliberate. Something was smeared onto my leg that caused it to end up like this. When it was first put on I didn't realise what it was going to do, but the pain just got more and more intense, burning and burrowing into the flesh. All I could do was stamp my feet, but that didn't help at all.' He shuddered and stamped his near fore in recollection, then laughing at himself for the involuntary action.

'Surely you could have got it off somehow.' This was meant more as a statement than a question.

'I thought so too at the time. But I hadn't really been paying attention to what had been going on, so I was rather caught out. When they applied the stuff I was tied up and what I hadn't noticed, was that something had been put around my neck, which meant that I could hardly move my head in any direction. I had got used to strange things being around me and nothing had hurt me before, so I wasn't worried when this contraption was put on. It was only when I went to scratch my leg that I realized I was trapped. As I dropped my head, so a series of wooden bars poked simultaneously into the underside of my jaw and neck. In panic I pulled my head back up again, but this time came up against the end of the halter rope. I don't know why but I just tugged at it to get away. Of course it didn't give way at first, not until all my weight was on it. Then, when it did finally part, it caught me completely off balance. My hind legs were right underneath me by then and, as my head shot up in the air, so I continued, right over the top, crashing down on the flat concrete floor behind me. It wasn't all that easy to get up again either. Not with that infernal cage around my neck. When I did get to my feet I was so stunned that all I could do was stand

169

petrified, not daring to move one way or the other.'

'Why Mole, why should anyone want to do this to you?' The whole situation didn't seem to make sense at all.

'Well, you don't know the whole story, but I had a serious injury in my leg, and I think this must have been part of the cure,' he said, looking down at his patchy lower limbs. 'I think you and I have turned this field into something of a recovery paddock,' he concluded.

Mole was good company although he always preferred eating to any other activity including conversation. I found it difficult to imagine that he had ever been energetic enough to cause himself any sort of injury. Every day, with the exception of those when there was a meet, Cid would be put into the adjoining field. If he had been out with the hounds the day before we would both gather at the fence and hear all about it. For Mole this was a particularly galling moment for in spite of his apparent laziness he too enjoyed his hunting, and he had just missed the entire season through his lameness. He had never offered to tell me how he had got so badly hurt, and it was some time after we had been put together that I actually got around to enquiring about it.

'It was during a race, believe it or not,' he told me, tongue-in-cheek.

'A race!' I uttered in astonishment, quite taken aback at the thought of Mole racing anything other than the growth rate of grass.

'It's not something I talk about often, because everybody reacts the way you have. But, it does happen to be true. I expect you immediately picture a racecourse but it wasn't like that. It was a race across country. Ordinary country, nothing prepared, starting at one point and going to another one about four miles away.'

'I am sorry to have shown such surprise, Mole, but you don't give the impression of being a racehorse, or anything like it.' Even now I felt that I was understating the case. His name alone suggested something much more sedentary than a racehorse, and he must have been given the name for a good reason. Perhaps the appellation had something to do with the way he munched his way through the grass, never lifting his head, never deviating, never pausing, just as if he were digging a tunnel that had no apparent end. Up till now I had always imagined it to be a description of his inability to move as a horse should.

'Don't worry, I am quite used to it. Besides it causes a few surprises now and then. A great many that day.' He chuckled at the memory.

'How far did you get before your leg got hurt?' I asked.

'All the way. Right to the finish,' he said proudly.

'You must have been very brave to have carried on in all that pain,' I told him.

'I would like to be able to tell you that I really had to grit my teeth, while the blinding shots of agonising pain racked my body. The truth is I didn't know I had done anything at all until I stood still for a while at the finish. Then a dull ache started in one leg. It increased in intensity as the swelling got bigger, settling to a dull pain that throbbed in time to my heartbeat. I certainly had no idea that it was bad enough to keep me away from hunting for a whole year.'

'So you don't even know how it happened.' I rather agreed with Mole that for all that time and pain there should be something more dramatic to tell.

'There are some possibilities, but the most likely is that I kicked into myself. There was a muddy field just towards the end of the race, and I know I was very tired by then, trying to catch the horse in front of me.' He stuck the offending leg forward, and bending down slightly, rubbed it with the side of his face, almost as if talking about the leg had made it irritate.

'Did you catch him?' I asked, but then, before he could reply, added, 'Better still tell me about the whole thing. Right from the start.'

'Gosh, it seemed such a long way. I am sure that we go even further hunting, but then there are lots of small breaks. Queuing for a jump, or waiting at a gateway—all sorts of little chances to get a quick rest. But on this trip—nothing. Had I known how far it was going to be when we started I would have gone a great deal slower for the first mile or so.'

'I suppose Mark was trying to slow you down all that time?' I pictured the two fighting each other over the pace.

'Yes, there were a few disagreements as I recall. Not with Mark though, he's Cid's boss. I am usually ridden by his brother, John,' Mole corrected me.

'I've never heard of him,' I said in genuine surprise.

'He isn't here all the time, just turns up now and then. So a lot of the time I am ridden by anybody who has got the time to spare, but I am really his horse,' explained Mole. 'Last year he rode me a lot though. Mostly to get us both fit for the race, although I didn't know it at the time. I still didn't know it was a race when we got to the start, although it was very puzzling.'

'If you had never been in a race before I should think it must be extremely confusing,' I agreed.

'No other race can possibly start in the same way as this one did, so I should think it would be puzzling to anyone,' he corrected me again. 'At first it was a bit like going hunting, except that we started warming up, jumping a few small hedges and cantering around. After a while a whistle blew, and all the horses were marshalled into three groups. These seemed to depend upon the weight of the rider. Then about thirty horses in the front rank took off and jumped over the first hedge. I was still watching to see where they were going when we also set off. Ours was by far the largest group. I would think there must have been around forty horses in all. The scramble to the first hedge was crazy. I remember that we got over it in the most undignified manner, whilst several others stopped and some went in almost the opposite direction, presumably to go across where it was a bit smaller. Three of us landed at more or less the same time, and we soon settled into line with myself in the middle.'

'At this stage I suppose you still hadn't worked out that it was a race you were in?' I asked.

'No, but I had seen the other group go, and I felt that we ought to be catching them up. Besides the one horse from our group who was in front was really pushing on, and I had no intention of letting him get away as well as all the others. All this time John was doing his best to settle me to a steady pace, but the pair of us were pulling away, dropping the third member from our group. We jumped some small rails, another hedge and a tiger trap which was almost hidden under some bushes in the corner of a field. From that tiger trap we went into a ploughed field, and the going became very heavy for a while, added to which we had to go through a series of gateways, which were very slippery and muddy, and finally over a bridge. By this time we were totally alone, having been left by the one horse and getting well away from the nearest pursuer. Across the next field, over a large hedge, all at a relaxed pace. Then, there in front of us was a mass of horses. Whatever was ahead had caused a lot of confusion. Horses were going in every direction. I just aimed for the middle of the bunch, which seemed to coincide with what John wanted. As we got amongst the group I could see that there was an enormous ditch, where the hedge had been cut out and over which we all had to pass. As we committed ourselves to the approach, another horse joined in on our right, but he was going at an angle to it, which was pushing me so far to the left that I doubted whether there would be enough room. I was contemplating an emergency stop when a third horse came at us from the left. I couldn't believe it! There we all were, three abreast, with poor old me fast becoming squashed in the centre.'

'It's a wonder that you didn't hurt yourself there,' I interjected.

'You might well be right, Norman,' he agreed. 'I wasn't going to give way to these queue jumpers, since I was the only one of the trio who had made a straight approach. So we all ended up at the edge of the ditch together, and what a ditch it was. The take-off was very rough, with bits of tree roots in it. The sides looked slimy, whilst the water in the bottom was pitch black. The horse who had come at it last, on my left, slithered to a halt in the last three strides, and didn't look as if he ever meant to get over. But the idiot who had come in from the right took off at the same time as myself, still not travelling straight. We met in the middle. All feet and reins. On landing we were hopelessly tangled, but I just leaned on him and hoped for the best. He tripped and I saw his nose dipping towards the ground as we recovered and went after the rest of the field.'

'Did you realize it was a race by now?' I wondered.

'If not officially, I certainly knew from the way that we had

173

pushed through the last obstacle that, one way or another, both of us intended to be at the front.'

'How close do you think you were to the front by now?' I enquired.

'A long way off I think. I could see a lot of horses ahead. From that big ditch the route was up a long gentle slope to a road crossing. John and I caught up with a large group of heavier horses at this point, just before having to jump either a metal gate or a tall hedge to the left of it. We had started to move to the left for the hedge, when one of those who had gone for the gate hit it so hard that it was ripped right off its hinges, falling flat to the ground. Naturally we quickly changed course and went through the open gap.'

'Whatever happened to the horse who hit the gate?' I enquired.

'He went sprawling on the grass, legs and hooves everywhere, but I don't think it was as bad as it was spectacular. The next part was amusing though, because all the riders had to get off their horses to cross the road at the top of the hill. But it wasn't a straight crossing. We came out of one gate, then had to trot down the road for a few metres before entering the next field. The jostling and fighting in the gateway to get onto the road reminded me of sheep being fed in the winter. They all try and get to the first bit of food to come from the bag, even jumping on each others backs to get to the front. Not that we did that, but I do remember one horse and his rider lying on their sides in the ditch at the side of the road, pushed out of the way by the flood that was following. When John got back on board we only had a handful of horses ahead of us, and most of those were crowding each other at a tiger trap, refusing and swinging about. Going to the left and jumping a hedge cut out this particular obstacle and suddenly we were up to third place. We followed the two leaders over the next pair of jumps, then suddenly we were on our own. The horse in the lead peeled off to the right, and I lost sight of him, while the one directly in front of us carried straight down the field that we had just got into. John and I turned slightly right handed, very shortly to cross a grass lane. Clearing the hedge on the first side put us down into it, two strides to cross it, when one should have

174

sufficed, and we were very close to the set of rails that was to take us out again. I hit them very hard as I strove to get up in the air, and felt them give beneath us. Our undignified arrival in the open did however show that there was no one in front of us at all. For all of that field and most of the next we were all alone, but then just as we got to a gateway a whole gaggle of horses came by us, going a lot faster than I could at that stage. Having been the clear leaders we had now been relegated to a lowly seventh. However, during the next mile four of those who had just got by were repassed as they had all gone too fast and had now 'blown-up'. The remainder were well ahead, but as we came into the last two fields, with the finish in sight, the one horse immediately in front of us slowed dramatically. A final burst would see us beat him and finish with a top three placing. He must have seen us coming, for at the last jump, which was only a few metres from the finish itself, he cut right across our path to force us to try and change sides and thus not manage to overtake. Having already had to jump with another horse touching me I couldn't see why I should not do the same again. We landed side by side. The other rider looked over at us. I can see his eyes now. Small, pig-like and hateful, his face shrouded in a red beard; nose and cheeks even redder. His obvious resentment kindled a last spark of energy and I just managed to cross the line ahead of him.'

'Then the pain must have become apparent.' My words had no visible reception. Mole had gone back to the scene of his triumph. 'Your leg must have started swelling then,' I tried again.

'Yes,' was all he said but then I suppose he had already told me about that, indeed about one of the cures he had been given.

'By the way you tell the tale, Mole, I would have said that you really enjoyed that race.' I didn't mention that he seemed to be going through all the excitement and emotion all over again. 'Probably a high point in your career. You are lucky to have been able to have done such exciting things, you know.'

'Umm. Well, I have been paying for it ever since. Then I suppose we have to pay for everything at some time or in some way. In a strange way it has made it even better—having to convalesce for a whole year afterwards.'

'Certainly makes a good tale,' I confirmed.

13
HOW IT SHOULD END

Mole suffered from an insatiable appetite. 'The grass is always greener on the other side' could have been a saying made with that particular horse in mind, for he would lean on fences to graze into the field beyond. In moments of extreme frustration at having some tasty morsel just out of reach, he would stand back from the wire and paw at it.

It was during one of these moments of frustration that he caught his hoof in the square section of fencing that formed the boundary on one side of the field. Pulling back in fright, he brought the entire section of fence—post and top strand of barb included—with him. The sight of this mass advancing towards him frightened him into turning to run away, thus ensuring that he was fully caught in the midst of it all. I was powerless to act, and had to stand and watch as the tangle went from bad to worse. A feeling of extreme frustation now overcame me as I could do no more than will him to stop and wait for help to arrive.

How he extricated himself I shall never know, for it had seemed to me that the situation was rapidly closing in on him the more he twisted and turned in the centre. Amazingly, Mole stopped and slowly walked away from the entanglement, but too late to avert damage to himself–cuts so deep that the white flesh showed through where the incision lay open, blood trickling in rivulets from the coronet down the face of the hoof,

Treatment for the injuries was a long time coming, as neither damage to horse nor fence was immediately noticed, there being no stock in the adjacent field and neither of us now feeling inclined to try and escape through the vast gap.

The day after Mole had been patched up, a complete stranger came into the field accompanied by Glyn. He reminded me of the dealer who had broken me to harness, in my native Wales. The same square shape and long stick with which he gesticulated when wishing to emphasise a particular point, or leaning heavily on it whilst in thought. He had an air about him that made us both back off as he approached. So that he could get a closer look, we were gently walked into a corner, and it was then, when the stranger could almost reach me with his stick, that I could smell on him the saline odour of blood. With my heart pounding I made the best escape I could, between Glyn and the fence. Mole followed at an even more awkward gait, not knowing which tattered leg to favour most. We must have made a comical sight, the two of us. Me, cantering with a swinging motion of the front legs, and him hobbling at an irregular trot. Neither of us stopped till we were in the middle of the field. We then looked back. Both men were still standing where we had left them. They watched us a moment longer, and then left the field. It was some time before either of us felt we could relax once more.

Glyn returned the following day, and I was taken up to the stables where Graham was waiting for me. Mole whinnied a sad farewell as I left him with the grazing to himself. Much to my surprise I was fitted with the collar and chains, after which we set off to work. We did not go far from the stable, only to Moat Wood, close to where the pheasants were kept. The trees here were small, and I was only required to take a small tush downhill. There was considerable stiffness from the very start, but the walking back up the hill to collect the next load was causing more difficulty than the work itself. At first I thought I would be able to cope with the pain, as the leg appeared to function moderately well, but I was very grateful for the end of the working day.

I did not go down to the stable that night, but up to the field with the broken-down barn in it. I recognised it instantly. The stout, but crumbling walls, the dew pond and the wizened oak tree. Nothing had changed, not even the grass had been eaten and it still lay coarse and tangled. I grazed for a while but found it dry and dull compared with the shorter and younger growth that Mole and I had enjoyed, so gave up and tucked myself close to the barn for the night. I heard the owl and a fox nearby, although they hardly reached beyond my subconscious, and I did little more than shuffle my feet all night long. It was only when I heard the banging of doors and spluttering of cars from the houses nearby that I made any real attempt to move.

The stiffness in the shoulder had never been so bad. When Graham came to collect me I had barely moved from the barn. Whistling to himself, he cheerfully fitted the harness, grabbed the rein and set off. I could not, and did not, follow; just braced myself for when the lead came tight. It did so with a suddenness that still jarred. Graham was swung round by the jolt and stared at me in amazement. He tried one more gentle tug, and when that didn't work he resigned himself to my immobility. It took all of that day to become at all mobile, and most of the next for them to get me back to the stables, where I received another visit from the vet. A less hurried approach this time, and a very thorough examination, which must have confirmed his worst fears as well as Glyn's. There was a sombre mood as they departed the stable, deep in conversation.

The melancholy disposition was by no means confined to Glyn and the vet. I fully realised that I could no longer work, and that my future must be very much in the balance—a feeling that was not in any way helped by finding the bottom field empty when I was taken to it later that day. I was surprised that Mole had not called to see me as I was led down the track, and even more amazed when he was not at the gate to greet me. When I was released I searched every corner for him, but all to no avail. Saddened by the disappointment of no equine company, I wandered aimlessly, nibbling here and there as I went. I had so fully expected to have found Mole that I had not given Cid a thought, and his sudden call from high above in the top field startled me.

'Norman!' he shouted. 'I thought you had gone back to work.'

We both converged on the water trough set in the fence between us, simultaneously seeing this as the appropriate meeting point.

'Where is Mole?' I immediately enquired.

'He left the same day as you, Norman,' Cid replied. 'That afternoon a small green lorry came. It parked in the gateway, down there,' he said, glancing to my right as an indication. 'They had a struggle to get him into it, ropes around his backside and a lot of heaving and shouting.'

'Was there a squarish-looking man with a long stick there?' I asked.

'He drove the lorry,' confirmed Cid.

'Poor Mole,' I muttered.

'What?' said Cid, not hearing.

'Oh, I just felt sorry for Mole, that's all,' I told him, and he looked rather puzzled, not aware of what I knew about the man with the long stick.

Some hope persisted, as I could have made all the wrong assumptions, so I was alert to the sound of horses' hooves and passing trailers or lorries. The day a trailer did come up to my gate and stop, my eyes were firmly fixed on it from the moment it arrived. The rear ramp was duly lowered and a large bay horse emerged. I instantly thought it must be Mole, and the excitement mounted within me. It was only when he turned to look in my direction that I realised it could not be Mole, for high on the forehead was a prominent star, easily visible from a long way off. At the same time I noticed that the coat was too dark a bay for Mole, as he had a much browner appearance than the new arrival. As he was led towards the gateway he held his head high, and walked with a swagger to his stride.

Rannoch! Who else but Rannoch moved with such grace and deliberation! I set off to meet him, calling as I went. Once released from his halter and in complete contrast to my laboured movements, he floated over the turf, throwing his feet forward, seeming to hang motionless in the air between each brief contact with the ground.

'You're sound!' I exclaimed in genuine astonishment.

'Of course,' he replied, even more surprised at my statement than I had been in making it. 'Why ever not?' he added.

I explained why I had come to think of this particular patch as a place for cripples only. How I had been injured against the tree. Mole, and his double accident and subsequent disappearance. My return to the field after trying to go back to the timber-tushing.

'Well, I have been here many times and never had anything wrong at all.' he confirmed. 'Mother and I have a break from each other at the end of every eventing season, and if the farm fields are full of stock then I come up here for part or all of the holiday,' he went on to explain.

For many days to come I was enthralled to hear about his exploits over the summer months, culminating in what he obviously took to be the biggest competition of his life, just the week previous to his vacation. To reach the competition he had travelled nearly all day, arriving at stables that were made out of canvas and which housed forty-eight horses, in six separate lines. Colourful cards and messages were pinned to the doors, whilst there were people around the stables all day and most of the night. How important he felt! The event itself sounded frightening, taking place in front of large crowds and lasting for three whole days.

'Mother was terrified before the Dressage,' he said. 'I could feel how rigid she had gone before we went in front of the crowd, whereas she normally loosens, bending her body movements to mine.'

The whole cross-country course was clearly something much bigger than anything he had ever seen previously. For the first two fences he had thought that it was going to be quite simple, but he had then come upon the most enormous drop. Whilst approaching, it was impossible to see over the edge and his description reminded me of the time that I was on top of Oldhill, with Abey, and we had all gone to hide in the quarry. It was difficult enough to walk over that edge, let alone contemplate jumping over it. The next two jumps involved crossing and re-crossing a large ditch, both times at acute angles. He even had to clear a large obstacle within a pond, his round ultimately coming to a temporary halt when he jumped onto a flat, timber surface that had been set in a ditch, not being able to keep his footing, and falling when landing on the bank at the far side.

'Mother and I got back together again, although we treated the rest of the course a little more circumspectly after that,' he said on reflection. 'Apart from a jump over a log into another pond, and a couple of corners, second from last, the worst was probably over.'

Before Rannoch left, we were joined by a mare who had also been an event horse, and the two of them spent many an hour comparing their past experiences. When Rannoch went back into training again, the mare was to stay on, and that spring she produced a fine foal, born in the middle of the night. These two were to remain all summer in the field, whilst a pony also joined us briefly, having come on loan to some children nearby. Cid, of course, was with us, until he started his hunting again.

So, you can see that I have taken on the role of grandfather to many horses. I am always here, happy in my retirement, which is what I had always wished for but doubted would happen. Others come and go, and so keep me in touch with the interesting and varied world of the horse.